A CHRISTIAN PANTOMIME

SCRIPT & SCORE
by
JEFF GRIST

RED
and the
WOLF

FULL SCORE

*Music, Songs
and Drama Script*

RED and The WOLF

A Christian Pantomime
by
Jeff Grist

FULL SCRIPT & MUSIC

MOORLEY'S Print & Publishing

ISBN 0 86071 503 5 (Full Score)
ISBN 0 86071 507 8 (Drama Script)

British Library Cataloguing in Publication Data.
A catalogue record for this book is available
from the British Library.

****

NOTE Regarding the Music.
In order to keep costs to the minimum two separate editions of this
Pantomime are produced. This Full Score contains music to all the songs and also includes a chord
only version of each. To avoid breaking the Copyright Law it is essential that
you do not copy any part of this book without the Publisher's written
permission. Permission for copying will be subject to a reproduction fee.

Published by:
MOORLEY'S Print & Publishing
23 Park Rd., Ilkeston, Derbys DE7 5DA
Tel/Fax: (0115) 932 0643

CHARACTERS:	
Red	Gus
Group of Children	Tanya
Mum	Spur
Grandma	Olaf
6 Travellers	Genie
Wolf	Agnes
Troy	6 Creatures + Leader

ACT ONE - SCENE ONE

[Introduction song]
"RED RIDING HOOD!"

Red riding hood said where she stood,
You must be good, Red riding hood.
It must be understood, even if you could,
You must be good, Red riding hood.

Red is only young. Full of joy and fun.
Sweet and innocent is she, as the day begun.
She just couldn't know how the day would go,
The sands of time are falling and the level's getting low!

You wonder if you should keep out of the wood,
You'd better be good, Red riding hood.
'Cause waiting in the wood, the wolf'll get you if he could,
You'd better be good, Red riding hood.

Very soon you'll see who has the victory.
The benefit of righteousness and truth will set you free.
The wolf howls and cries with evil in his eyes,
Take no heed unto his words, don't listen to his lies.

Our little girly Red unfortunately said
she would trust the hairy one and soon she is misled.
But because the Bible say, the dark was held at bay
and Red and all her friends would see good will win the day.

Anybody could keep out of the wood, learn to live good,
Red riding hood. Live as you would, or as you should,
Live and do good, Red riding hood.

Scene:Enter Red being followed by group of children. They are playing "What's the time, Mr Wolf?"

Group: What's the time, Mr Wolf?

Red: One o'clock!

Group: What's the time, Mr Wolf?

Red: Two o'clock!

Group: What's the time, Mr Wolf?

Red: Three o'clock!

Boy: (to girl) What time is it when you go to the dentist?

Girl: Dunno.

Boy: Tooth hurty!!

Group: What's the time, Mr Wolf?

Red: Four o'clock!

Group: What's the time, Mr Wolf?

Red: Five o'clock!

Girl: *(to boy)* What time is it when an elephant sits on your fence?

Boy: I don't know.

Girl: Time to get a new fence!

Group: What's the time, Mr Wolf?

Red:	Six o'clock!
Boy:	What time is it when a mouse sits on your fence?
Girl:	Don't know.
Boy:	Time to get a new elephant!
Group:	What's the time, Mr Wolf?
Red:	Seven o'clock!
Group:	What's the time, Mr Wolf?
Red:	Eight o'clock!
Girl:	*(points up into air)* Look! A clock with wings!
Boy:	*(looking frantically)* Where?
Girl:	There! Doesn't time fly when you're enjoying yourself?
Group:	What's the time, Mr Wolf?
Red:	Nine o'clock!
Boy:	What ticks but doesn't keep time?
Girl:	I don't know.
Boy:	Ticky tape!
Group:	What's the time, Mr Wolf?
Red:	Ten o'clock!
Girl:	What's the difference between a jeweller and a jailer?
Boy:	I dunno.
Girl:	One sells watches and the other watches cells!
Group:	What's the time, Mr Wolf?
Red:	Eleven o'clock!
Group:	What's the time, Mr Wolf?
Red:	*(turns and snarls)* Dinner time!!! *(The children scream and scatter. Red chases them for a while, then stops.)* Wait a minute! It's alright! Come back! Did I scare you?
Group:	Yes!!
Red:	There's no need to be afraid! *(Music starts. They all sing, "Who's afraid of the big, bad wolf?")*

"WHO'S AFRAID OF THE BIG, BAD WOLF?"

Chorus:	Who's afraid of the big, bad wolf? The big, bad wolf? The big, bad wolf? Who's afraid of the big, bad wolf? Tra la la la la.
Red:	Once the wolf came after me, thought he'd have me for his tea! What a fearful sight to see.
Group:	Tra la la la la.
Red:	I asked him if he had a thirst, suggested he drink some water first. Filled him up, thought he would burst.
Group:	Tra la la la la.

4

Red: What the wolf just didn't see,
he thought he took water from me.
I really gave him T.C.P.

Group: Tra la la la la.

Red: He walks the woods from length to breadth,
can find no one to scare to death,
'cause everyone can smell his breath.

Group: Tra la la la la.

[Song ends]

(Enter Mum from cottage)

Mum: Red! Red!

Red: Yes mum?

Mum: Come here! I've got something for you!

Red: Okay! *(to children)* I've got to go. See you later!

Group: Yeah okay! Bye!!

(Group leaves. Red runs to cottage and joins mum)

Red: Yes mum?

Mum: *(brings out package from behind back)* Happy birthday darling!

Red: *(takes present)* Oh, thanks mum! But my party's not until this afternoon!

Mum: Well, I want you to have this now! It's special!

Red: Okay! *(rips open parcel to reveal book)* The Holy Bible!
It's very nice mum but what do I want a bible for?

Mum: It's more than just a book, you know! It's the living word of God!

Red: *(holds it at arms length)* It lives??

Mum: Yes! But it won't hurt you, silly! It will protect and guide you. Whatever situation you get yourself in, the Word will always help you out! You must trust the Word of the Lord!

Red: But I just thought it was all stories!

Mum: It's a lot more than that! *(Music starts and mum sings "His Word!" song)*

"HIS WORD!"

The Bible's a book about prophets. There's bravery and battles galore.
But read it with more understanding to find out what it's all for!

His Word is the book of ages. Inspired by God and food for the soul.
A light in darkness and a saving power. Hope to men to achieve their goal.

It's about the works of the Father and of all the good things He's done.
How he secured our salvation by sacrificing His Son.

His Word is a crushing hammer, life-giving force and devouring flame.
Loved by the saints, blessed seed for the sower.
Trustworthy and sure the same.

It's full of God's great wonders. Incredible, miraculous tales.
It holds promises never broken, and a love that never fails.

His Word is full of knowledge. Wisdom for aged, wisdom for youth.
Sword and protector, life purifier. Word of God, holder of truth.

[Song ends.]

Red: I never realised what a powerful book this is!

Mum: Well, now you know! Keep it with you, always. Let it be your standard and your guide.

Red: My standard? What's a standard?

Mum: A standard is a set of rules or morals that you establish in your life. You follow them closely, live by them and never break them!

Red: Have we all got standards?

Mum: Yes, but that's where people go wrong! We all have different standards. This causes envy and confusion.

Red: I don't understand! Why must we all have the same standards? Why must we have rules at all?

Mum: Watch your friends playing there. After you've seen them, I think you'll understand!

(As they watch, a girl enters and plays with her toys. A small see-through pot of what looks like raisins sits on a rock)

Girl: Tra la la! What a beautiful day! The sun is shining. The birds are singing. The cows are mooing. The pigs are grunting, and dad is sleeping. That's why I'm thrown out to play! Still, never mind. It's a lovely day! *(Dolls head comes off in her hand)* Oh no! My head's come off! What am I to do?
Dr Ted! Dr Ted! Come quick!
(She brings teddy round from behind her back and assumes lower 'male' voice) What seems to be the problem? *(higher voice)* What do you mean? Can't you see? *(Lower voice)* Okay, okay! Keep your hair on! *(high)* Very funny! *(low)* You've got to keep a cool head in these situations! *(high)* Oh no!! *(low)*
Let's have a look then! Hmm! We'd better HEAD over to the hospital! Still, it's only a flesh wound. Nothing to worry your sweet HEAD about! *(high)* That's not funny doctor!
(low) Still, it must be a weight off your shoulders! We'll go by helicopter! *(high)* I can't doctor! *(low)* Why not? *(high)* I haven't a head for heights! Ha! Ha! *(low)* That's the spirit! Laugh and the whole world laughs at you!
(high) Well, it's the only way to get ahead!

(Enter boy.)

Boy: Are you talking to yourself again?

Girl: I'm playing, silly!

Boy: You're plain stupid! *(walks to one side)*

Girl: Oh yeah? And I suppose what you're doing is better, is it?

Boy: Yep!

(Pause.)

Girl: What ARE you doing?

Boy: Exploring!

Girl: Exploring what?

Boy: My territory! This is uncharted land! I'm looking for treasure, but I've got to look out for natives, especially ones with headless voodoo dolls. *(indicates doll)*

Girl: *(tries to hide doll)* Very funny, I don't think!

Boy: *(notices pot)* What's this? *(picks it up and unscrews lid)* A new kind of fruit? I think I'll call them... Raisins!

Girl: We've already got raisins! And anyway, you shouldn't eat them. They're somebody else's!

Boy: They won't miss a few! *(tucks into pot.)* Yum, yum! Why don't you come over and play with me?

Girl: Not allowed!

Boy: What d'yah mean?

Girl: I'm not allowed past this point! Mum said!

Boy:	Why not?
Girl:	So that they know where I am!
Boy:	Oh! I'm allowed to play right up to here!
Girl:	That's not fair!
Boy:	Not my fault!
Girl:	Not fair!
Boy:	Well, come over anyway! They won't know!
Girl:	No! It's wrong! I'll have a row!
Boy:	Suit yourself! *(prances back and fore over girl's boundary)*
	(Enter boy 2, carrying something clenched in his fist. He looks fed up)
Boy 2:	Hi!
Both:	Hi!
Girl:	Where have you been?
Boy 2:	Oh, I've been collecting!
Girl:	Collecting what?
Boy 2:	Spiders!!
Girl:	Urghh!!
Boy:	Ha, ha! Sissy! Who's afraid of spiders then?
Boy 2:	Yeah, I collect them!
Girl:	Don't they ever escape?
Boy 2:	Nah! I pull off their legs and put them in a pot! *(sees pot in boys hand)* That's it there! *(Boy begins to choke and puts pot down. Boy 2 picks it up)* Funny? I had lots more than this earlier!
Girl:	Ha, ha, ha!!
Boy:	I don't feel very well!
Girl:	*(starts singing)* Incy wincy spider climbs up the water spout. Here comes the boy and stuffs him down his throat!
Boy:	Stop it!!
Boy 2:	*(to boy)* Have you been eating them?
Boy:	Yes!
Boy 2:	*(offers pot)* Want another?
Boy:	*(in horror)* No!! *(runs off stage to girl's laughter)*
Girl:	That was funny!
Boy 2:	*(sadly)* Yeah!
Girl:	Hey? Where've you been, anyway?
Boy 2:	Oh, I don't know! Well past the woods!
Girl:	Past the woods? Are you allowed to play that far?
Boy 2:	I suppose so! My folks haven't said I couldn't! They just said it's up to me to decide!
Girl:	That sounds exciting!

Boy 2: Well, it was at first! I could go for miles. But sometimes I'd get lost, and scared! There's a wolf out there, you know! I just wish mum and dad would give me a limit, so that I'd know when I'd gone too far! Then I couldn't get lost! I'd know when I was right and when I was wrong! I really don't like having to decide for myself! It doesn't seem right. And at least then I'd know that they care enough about me to want to know where I am!

Girl: Well, I'm glad I'm only allowed to play this far! Why don't you play with me?

Boy 2: Can I?

Girl: Yes, but there's one small condition!

Boy 2: What's that?

Girl: Lose the spiders!

Boy 2: Okay! *(Throws them away)*

Girl: Let's go!

(They exit)

Mum: So you see Red, different standards cause confusion and jealousy! And having no standards at all leaves you isolated and feeling uncared for. We all need to know when we're right or wrong, even if we won't do anything about it!

Red: And God's standard *(holds up Bible)* is a good one to keep to?

Mum: It's the best standard because it's for everyone. It treats everyone the same, regardless of race, creed or colour!

Red: Thanks mum! It's a wonderful present!

Mum: That's my pleasure! Now, let's go and get ready for your party. Grandma will be here soon! Come on!

[They both exit into the cottage]

[END OF SCENE ONE]

ACT ONE - SCENE TWO

Scene: Mum and Red sit outside the cottage. Enter Grandma.

Gran: Cooeee! Anybody home?

Mum: *(to Red)* Oh well, Grandma's here!

Red: Why don't you and Grandma get along better?

Mum: Well, I'm not saying Grandma's a mean person, but she's the sort who'd go to a home for the blind and stamp the braille flat!

Red: *(indignantly)* Mum!

Mum: And she has a road sweeper mind.

Red: How do you mean?

Mum: It's always in the gutter!

Red: Mum!!

Mum: We get along fine. Now, go and meet Grandma!
(Red runs and greets Gran)

Gran: Hello my darling!

Red: Hello Gran! *(they hug)* Mum and I were just saying how much we are looking forward to your visit. *(Mum coughs)*

Gran: *(looking up at mum)* Yes, I'm sure! *(to Red)* Anyway, let me sit down a minute. *(to mum)* Hello dear!

Mum: Hello Mummy! *(goes to kiss cheek but misses)*

Gran: Well well! Look at that dress!

Mum: Do you like it? It's just something I threw on!

Gran: Yes, and you nearly missed! Hardly befitting someone of forty-five, is it!

Mum: *(to Red, horrified)* I don't look forty-five, do I?

Gran: Not any more!

Mum: *(still to Red)* I dread the thought of my forty-fifth birthday!

Gran: Why? What happened then?

Mum: You know I'm not forty-five yet!

Gran: You may as well be, the state you're in! *(to Red)* Every girl has the right to be ugly, but she's abused the privilege!

Mum: Mother!!

Gran: Do you know, when she was born, she was so ugly, the doctor slapped me!

Red: Gran!!

Mum: That's it! I'm not going to bite!

Gran: Thank goodness for that! I wouldn't want to catch anything!

Mum: I've learnt that in a battle of wits, never fight an unarmed person!

Gran: I just can't help myself!

Red: Gran!!

Gran: Oh, we're just bantering! Come here and let me look at you!
(Red stands) You look wonderful! *(to mum)* You sure she's yours?
(mum ignores her) And it's your birthday today, so I've brought you this! *(brings out present)* I've made it myself! Go on! Open it!!

(Red opens present and takes out red riding hood)

Red: Gran, it's wonderful! Thank you!

Gran: Happy birthday, darling. Let's put it on you to check it fits!

(As they do so, mum appears with birthday cake, candles lit)

Mum: *(sings)* Happy birthday to you, happy birthday to you.
Happy birthday dearest daughter, happy birthday to you!

Gran: I hear your singing hasn't improved!

Mum: *(to Red)* Make a wish and blow out the candles!

Gran: I wish you'd stop singing!

Mum: *(to Gran)* Not you!!

(Red blows out candles. Mum starts to cut cake)

Mum: Oh, I love birthdays! It just doesn't seem all that long ago since you were my little baby!

Gran: I don't want to be reminded of when you were a kid.

Red: Tell me of that time, mum!

Mum: Very well! *(music starts. Mum and Gran sing song)*

"MUM AND GRANDMA'S SONG."

Mum: You're my little girl, my life and my world,
you fill my heart with joy!
Gran: You made me a wreck, were a pain in the neck,
and besides, I wanted a boy!
Mum: You put a smile on my lips.
Gran: You put a mile on my hips.
Mum: you make me complete through and through.
Both: But there's no denying and I wouldn't be lying
when I say that I love you!

Mum: I was once all forlorn but then you were born
and filled my world with light!
Gran: I was reasonably happy till you filled your nappy
and left me an 'orrible sight!
Mum: I watched you grow up.
Gran: I watched you throw up.
Mum: There's nothing that I wouldn't do,
Both: But there's no denying and I wouldn't be lying,
when I say that I love you!

Mum: Ah, the way that you look, the way that you speak,
you are just good as gold!
Gran: Urgh! You're a terrible cook, and the way that you shriek,
makes my blood turn cold.

Mum: You gave me such pride as you sat by my side,
and I sang as you slept in my lap.
Gran: You gave me labour pains and varicose veins
and a belly that looks like a map!
Mum: Not to mention the smiles.
Gran: Not to mention the piles.
Mum: And the hugs and kisses too!
Both: But there's no denying and I wouldn't be lying
when I say that I love you.

Mum: Ah, the things that you do, your sweet little ways,
you're a wonder to see!

Gran: Urgh! You're a silly young moo, but then one of these days,
you'll get old, just like me! He! He!

Mum: You're a gift from above, a showering of love,
we're a song and you are the verse.

Gran: With your shrieks and your yells and your strange funny
smells, I wondered if life could get worse!

Mum: Sometimes life has been flat.

Gran: But despite all of that.

Both: The one thing that always rings true, is that there's no
denying and I wouldn't be lying when I say that I love you.

Mum: Yes there's no denying,

Gran: and I wouldn't be lying,

Both: When I say that I love you!!

(Song ends)

Gran: Urgh! I've got a bitter taste in my mouth!

Mum: Probably bit your tongue!

Gran: *(getting up)* I see you haven't lost yours. *(looks at wall)*
What's this then? Another one of your silly abstract paintings?

Mum: No, it's a mirror!

Red: *(trying to stave off the argument)* Gran? Your face looks lovely and smooth!

Gran: *(looking in mirror)* Thank you dear! I tried one of those facial mudpacks! I felt it improved my looks!

Mum: Yes, then the mud fell off!

Gran: *(sitting down again)* Very funny! Anyway, where did you get that mirror from? Did you steal it?

Mum: No I did not steal it!

Gran: She was always a bit of a tea leaf, your mother, even from the day she was born! They said, she's got her mother's eyes, her father's nose, the doctor's wallet!

Mum: Everyone says I got my good looks from my father!

Gran: Rubbish! Your father wasn't a plastic surgeon!

Mum: Anyway, I was never a thief! You always made up tales about me! Like that time you told everyone I was deaf and dumb!

Gran: That's not true! I never said you were deaf!

Mum: I would never steal anything! I have had to make a living by my wits!

Gran: Well, half a life is better than none!

Mum: I am a self-made woman!

Gran: But why make yourself like that?

Mum: Eh?

Gran: Still, that relieves the Almighty of a great responsibility!

Mum: What I'm saying is, all that I am or will be, I owe to my father!

Gran: It's a pity we couldn't send him the five pence and settle the account!

Red: Er, let's play a party game!

Mum: *(to gran)* Let's play horse! I'll be the front end, you just be yourself!

Gran: Cheek! If you're such a catch, how come you haven't remarried?

Mum: You know very well that I almost got married again ten years ago!

Red: You never told me! What happened?

Mum: Well, we got as far as the wedding day. We stood before the vicar, about to say the vows when suddenly my fiance ran out! And I never heard from him again!

Red: Aw! How sad! Did he lose his nerve?

Gran: No, he found it again!

Mum: Anyway, since then, I've been asked to get married loads of times!

Red: Really? Who asked you?

Gran: Me mainly!

Mum: (dreamily) Well, two Christmases ago, Thomas kissed me under mistletoe.

Gran: I wouldn't kiss you under anaesthetic!

Red: Gran!!

Mum: He said I reminded him of the ocean!

Red: Do you mean wild, restless and romantic?

Gran: No, she made him feel sick! He! He!

Mum: He liked my dresses! He said I looked a million dollars!

Gran: Yes, all green and crinkly!

Mum: But it wasn't to be! I told him, "I've got good news and bad news! Firstly, I'm not marrying you!"

Red: What did he say?

Gran: What's the bad news?

Mum: Since I refused to marry him, he's been drinking heavily!

Gran: Isn't that carrying the celebration a little too far?

Mum: I'll have you know that a lot of men are going to be really miserable when I wed!

Gran: Why? How many are you marrying?

Red: Gran!!!

Mum: There's no talking to you when you're like this!

Gran: Hallelujah! She's got the message!

Mum: Well you're not funny! You couldn't even entertain a doubt!

Gran: Ooooooh! Well maybe you could entertain these people coming along now! Play your cards right and you could be in here! You've got a one in six chance!

(Enter six travellers)

Trv1: Hello? What have we here? A party?

Mum: (making herself more presentable) Yes! It's my daughter's birthday party! Won't you join us?

Gran: Why? Are we coming apart?

Mum: Quiet mother!

Trv1: Well, we don't mind if we do!

Red: Please sit down and have some cake!

Gran: (points to mum) If she made it, watch out for the file!

Trv1: We'd love some cake!

Trv2: And something to drink, please!

Mum:	Of course!
Trv3:	But we have no money!
Red:	That doesn't matter!
Trv4:	But it does to us.
Trv5:	So, we have an alternative!
Gran:	A what?
Trv6:	An alternative way of payment.
Trv1:	And it's especially nice to pay this way as it's such a pretty girl's birthday!
All:	We will entertain you! *(The travellers split up into pairs and each pair performs an act. At the end, they all join together for the song!)*
Trv1:	Ladies and gentlemen, my friend and I would like to host a contest of brain versus balance. My friend will balance this broom on one finger whilst I reel off some limericks! The contest ends when either I run out of limericks or he drops the broom! *(to Trv2)* Are you ready? *(Trv2 starts to balance broom)* Here we go!

> "There once was a pious young priest,
> who lived almost wholly on yeast,
> 'For,' he said,'It is plain we must all rise again,
> and I want to get started at least!'"

(to Trv2) Still going? Okay!

> "There was a young monk of Siberia,
> who of fasting grew wearier and wearier,
> till at length with a yell he burst from his cell,
> and devoured the Father Superior!"

Not getting tired are we? Right!

> "A silly young man from the Clyde,
> in a funeral procession was spied,
> when asked, 'Who is dead?' He giggled and said,
> 'I don't know! I just came for the ride!'"

Hey? What's that over there? Aha! Nearly looked!

> "There was a young boy from the choir,
> whose voice went up higher and higher,
> till one Sunday night it vanished from sight,
> and they found it next day on the spire!"

Are you still there? Um, um, okay!

> "There was an old fellow of Trinity,
> a doctor well versed in Divinity,
> but he took to free thinking and then to deep drinking,
> and soon had to leave the vicinity!" Boom! Boom!

(On second "Boom!", he bumps into Trv2 who drops brush!)

Ah well, contest over! *(to Trv3+4)* Over to you!

(Both Trv3 and 4 hold a glass of water in their hands)

Trv3:	Thank you, thank you! I would like to take this opportunity to prove how gullible my friend here is!
Trv4:	Eh? Hold on! I'm not Gulliver!
Trv3:	No, no! My silly chum! Gullible, I said. Gullible!
Trv4:	Oh, I'm sorry!
Trv3:	That's alright! So, as I was saying.....

Trv4: Wait!

Trv3: What?

Trv4: Did you say I'm gullible?

Trv3: Yes!

Trv4: I'm not gullible!

Trv3: Oh no?

Trv4: No!

Trv3: You sure?

Trv4: Positive!

Trv3: What time is it?

Trv4: It's..... *(looks at watch and pours water over himself)*

Trv3: You see, Ladies and Gentlemen, the proof! Only Mr Gullible would have fallen for that one!

Trv4: *(dripping)* Okay! Okay! I get the picture!

Trv3: Oh really?

Trv4: Yeah! I'm not as dumb as you make out!

Trv3: No?

Trv4: No! In fact, I reckon you're just as gullible as me!

Trv3: Oh yes?

Trv4: Yes!

Trv3: Go on then! Prove it!

Trv4: Okay! What time is it?

Trv3: *(wears watch on inside of wrist. When he looks, he pours water over Trv4.)* It's about eight fifteen!

Trv4: This is bad!

Trv3: I thought it was good!

Trv4: I didn't read about this in my horoscope!

Trv3: What's that? You read a horoscope?

Trv4: Yeah?

Trv3: Talk about being gullible!

Trv4: Well, I like to know what's going to happen, don't I!

Trv3: Two points! One! You're not supposed to know because that knowledge will govern your future decisions. You will be in bondage to the knowledge and not free! And two! It's rubbish! And if it was true, it would be terribly inaccurate!

Trv4: How do you mean?

Trv3: Do you mean to tell me that if your stars say you are going to get promotion today, that one twelfth of the world's population can expect a pay rise? It's nonsense!

Trv4: But I need to know!

Trv3: Okay, okay! You don't need horoscopes!

Trv4: No?

Trv3: No! I will help you develop a sense to predict what's going to happen!

Trv4: What? You?

Trv3: Yep! You just do as I say and you'll amaze yourself!

Trv4: Alright!

Trv3: Okay! Now, first of all, are you ticklish?

Trv4: What's that got to do with it?

Trv3: Uh,uh! Remember? Do as I say!

Trv4: Okay!

Trv3: Now, are you ticklish?

Trv4: Yes!

Trv3: Good! That's the preparation set up!

Trv4: You're not going to tickle me, are you?

Trv3: Just do as I say! Now, take off your shirt!

Trv4: Eh?

Trv3: Go on! Take off your shirt!

Trv4: I'm not taking my shirt off in front of all these people!

Trv3: They won't mind! Will you? No! See? Ditch the shirt!

Trv4: Why?

Trv3: It helps to feel the sensations!

Trv4: *(starts taking shirt off)* You're right!

Trv3: See?

Trv4: I feel a nerd already!

Trv3: That's better! Now turn around and raise both arms high into the air!

Trv4: You won't tickle me, will you! It's just that I'll lose control and wet myself!

Trv3: Just do it! Come on! Turning around helps you to blank off from everything that might distract you, and raising your arms helps you to develop the sense!

Trv4: But.....!

Trv3: *(firmly)* Go on! Do it! You'll be glad you did!

Trv4: *(reluctantly)* Okay! *(turns round and slowly puts arms into the air.)*

Trv3: Right! Now concentrate! You should be starting to feel something!

Trv4: No!

Trv3: *(moves in closer)* Are you sure?

Trv4: No!

Trv3: Well, try this! *(tickles Trv4 under the arms)*

Trv4: *(drops arms and turns round quickly)* I knew you were going to tickle me!

Trv3: See? It's working already! Here, put your shirt on!
   (Trvs3+4 step back while Trvs 5+6 step forward)

Trv5: Thank you! We also have a contest! My friend and I have three custard pies each. Without actually throwing them at each other, we must contrive a way of making sure that all three pies are splattered on the opponent! The first to do so is the winner!

Trv6:　Correct!

Trv5:　(*drops plate on floor*)　Now then! Oh dear, look! I've dropped a plate. Please pick it up for me!

Trv6:　Certainly!

(*As Trv6 goes to pick up plate, he kicks it forward. Meanwhile Trv5 has picked up a pie and holds it upside down over Trv6 head. When Trv6 stands up, he puts his head into the pie!*)

Trv5:　Well, that's one to me! Pretty easy!

Trv6:　I didn't know we'd started!

Trv5:　Didn't I say go?

Trv6:　No!

Trv5:　Silly me! Still, we've started now!

Trv6:　(*scraping pie from back of head*) So I notice!

Trv5:　(*picks another two pies*) So you see how the game is played, Ladies and Gentlemen! Just these two pies to go! (*He walks over to Trv6 with one pie held high over his head, the other lower*)

Trv6:　Eh, you're not allowed to drop it on me!

Trv5:　I won't! By the way, your zip's undone!

Trv6:　Eh? (*looks down and face straight into lower pie*)
(*Trv6 walks away with one pie left, looking very pleased with himself. Starts to boast to Red and crowd. Meanwhile, Trv6 brings all pies together in a small line in the floor and kneels right behind Trv5. When Trv5 turns around, he can't stop himself from falling over Trv6 and falls into three pies, plus his own*)

Trv6:　(*jumps to feet*) The winner!

(*All travellers clap*)

Trv1:　And speaking of pies and such like, we'd like to sing a little song about food for you! Ready lads?
(*they sing*)

"DON'T GO DOWN TO THE CAKE SHOP, MUM!"

When I was a little boy, my mother said to me,
if you eat your greens and meat, there's ice cream after tea.
A sticky bun is lots of fun. We'll wash it down with pop,
and follow it with biscuit and the odd chocolate drop!

Don't go down to the cake shop mum, I've had enough to eat!
I've had my fill of fairy cakes and other things so sweet.
There's flab and fat where muscle sat, my belly's on the floor.
Don't go down to the cake shop mum, I can't take any more!

The breakfast treat was shredded wheat with strawberries and cream,
buttered toast, ham honey roast and pancakes by the ream,
chicken legs, chips and eggs would quickly follow brunch,
a four course meal of lamb and veal would satisfy for lunch!

Don't go down to the cake shop mum, I'm feeling rather sick!
If I eat another cake, I'll look like Moby Dick!
Captain Ahab will try to stab the mountain that is me,
Don't go down to the cake shop mum, I've had enough for tea!

Next at three, afternoon tea of bread and bramble jam,
a little snack, and then a rack of ribs from roasted lamb.
We're in the mood for Chinese food with chicken chop suey,
What would be nice is special fried rice, in fact a meal for three!

Don't go down to the cake shop mum, I've no hunger or thirst.
If anything should pass my lips, I think that I would burst!
Believe or not, my teeth have rot, my heart is asking "Why?"
Don't go down to the cake shop mum, I think I'd rather die!!

(*End of song*)

Red: Thank you! Thank you for making my birthday so special!
Now, I would like to give you all something for the rest of your journeys! It is a passage from the Word of Life! It may not seem much now, but I trust that should you ever need it, it will encourage and strengthen you. *(to Trv1)*
"Therefore I tell you, whatever you ask for in prayer,
believe that you have received it, and it will be yours!"
(Trv2,3,4 and 5) And for you, "When you pass through the
waters, I will be with you; and when you pass through the
rivers, they will not sweep over you. When you walk through
the fire, you will not be burned; the flames will not set
you ablaze!"

Trvs: Thank you.

Red: *(to Trv6)* And for you,
"A righteous man may have many troubles, but the Lord delivers him from them all!"

Trv6: Thank you very much!

Gran: Well, I'd better be heading back before it gets too dark!

Mum: Oh, what a shame!

Trv1: Madam, we are also travelling the path! May we escort you!

Gran: Why? Lost your way?

Mum: Mother!!!

Trv1: No! But with the six of us with you, your passage may be safer!

Gran: Very well! I don't know, so many men, so little time!
(stands and kisses Red) Goodbye darling!

Red: Goodbye Gran, and thank you again!

Gran: My pleasure. Make sure you wear the hood now. It'll keep you warm!

Red: I will!

Gran: *(to mum)* And goodbye dear, until next time!

Mum: Goodbye mother! Safe trip!

All: Goodbye and thank you! Last one to the path is a rotten egg!

Red: Bye.

(The travellers and Grandma exit and so do Red and Mum)

END OF SCENE.

ACT ONE - SCENE THREE

Mum: Red! Red!

Red: Yes mum?

Mum: Oh Red! Listen darling, I've got to send you on an errand! Grandma's been taken ill!

Red: What's wrong?

Mum: Apparently, a snake snapped at her!

Red: That's strange! Snakes usually coil and strike, not snap!

Mum: This was a garter snake! Anyway, it was quite a nasty bite!

Red: Oh no!

Mum: Yes! I didn't know that grandma's teeth were so good! She nearly bit the snake in half!

Red: Eh?

Mum: Yes! She felt sorry for the poor thing after that and took it to the vets. But it was pouring with rain and she's caught a cold! She had to seek medical advice.

Red: What did the doctor say?

Mum: Bad news, I'm afraid! Looks like the snake isn't going to pull through!

Red: No, about grandma!

Mum: Oh, she's as fit as a fiddle! He reckons she'll outlive us all! Mind you, I believe him. She'll be the death of me!!

Red: Mum!!

Mum: Anyway, she has to spend a few days in bed, so I want you to take some provisions, to stock up her cupboards and keep her going! *(hands Red a basket)*

Red: Yum! What's she got?

Mum: Prunes! That'll keep her going!

Red: No really!

Mum: Oh, her usual stuff! Bat's wings, frog's blood, eye of newt, that sort of stuff!

Red: Mum!!

Mum: Well, she's got to have a "spell" in bed!

Red: *(looks in basket)* Cakes, pies and fruit!

Mum: Yes! That'll last her a while!

Red: Okay!

Mum: Now, before you go, I must warn you. Grandma's house is along the path of truth. Stay on the path and you can't miss it! But it cuts through the woods of deception, which is a very dangerous place! Stay on the path! Don't go in the woods!

Red: Right! The path of truth cuts right through deception! Got it!

Mum: And watch out for any strange creatures. I've been told that there's a wolf prowling around there. Be especially careful of him!

Red: Why? What harm can he do?

Mum: He'll try and coax you into deception woods, and eat you!

Red: Okay! I'll watch out for him! *(to audience)* And you'll help, won't you boys and girls?

Mum: Good! Now, before you go, take my advice!

(Music starts and they sing "Stay on the path of truth!")

"STAY ON THE PATH OF TRUTH!"

Mum sings

Now you're going on a journey and you'll be all on your own,
travelling past deception woods, miles from any phone.
Be courteous to who you meet but never ever stop.
Go straight through until the end. Don't let your standards drop!

Chorus

Wherever life will take you, let this be your journey's guide,
stay on the path of truth and don't go off the side!

Mum sings

Though lying's very tempting, let me tell you 'bout our Jim.
On a job application found it asked if he could swim.
Well he really wanted work. He nearly said that this was so,
but found out it was "deep sea diving" and decided to say "No!"

Now Patrick had lunch down his local when he had his little scare
'cause his wife phoned up the barmaid to see if he was there.
Said Pat, "You haven't seen me!" and he tucked into his grub.
You can imagine his face when he found out that his wife phoned from the pub!!

Drunken Horace stumbled home one night. He'd slipped and cut his back.
Looked in the bathroom mirror to plaster up the crack.
He hadn't woken Nelly. Crept to bed and thought he'd pass,
but the silly fool had missed and put the plaster on the glass!

Red sing

I've listened to your teaching and I'll do just as you say,
and I'll return as quickly by the end of the day.
I really don't want to get lost where I can't be traced,
rest assured, I'll do my best not to be caught red-faced!

(Song ends. Red waves goodbye and exits)

END OF SCENE.

ACT ONE - SCENE FOUR

(Enter wolf who sings his song)

"WOLF'S SONG!"

Hi! It's me! Welcome to my world of obscurity.
Oh hi! Again! Stop and have a chat, you can be my friend.
Everyone is equal here 'cause nobody's of worth,
and by the time I'm finished here, you'll be damned upon the
earth, so Hi!

Hello! Good day! But that won't last too long if I have my way.
Bonjour! Hola! Chow, buonos dias, even bore dda!
I know all the languages beneath this cursed sun.
You can't say that I'm prejudiced 'cause I hate everyone, so Ha!
I mean, Hi!

People don't understand me! They think that killing's my goal.
But that depends on my hunger! What I'm really after's your soul!

So hi! Come in! Let me introduce you to a world of sin.
This way! Follow me! There are wonders in the wood, just come and see!
Step into the thicket and have a little nap.
Then when you awaken, you'll find you're in my trap!
So Hi! Oh Hi! My my!!

(Song ends)

Wolf: What a glorious day for eating, ha, ha! Two fieldmice and a hedgehog doesn't go far for breakfast, so I'm ready for dinner! I particularly like children! Are there any children in the audience? *(crowd yells "No!")* Are you sure?
(crowd yells "Yes!") I'm sure I can see children! *(goes towards front row)* I only want a little taste! Just a nibble! Just a chomp! I promise I'll chew properly! I'll take my time! I won't just "wolf" it down! I do have manners. Some people say that my manners are just a front!
They say I'm a wolf in sheep's clothing! Well, that's nonsense! I wouldn't be caught dead in a sheepskin coat, unless I was eating the sheep at the time! But now I'm hungry, and there's no telling what I'd do! Ha, ha! I once ate a vicar, but I was sick! It just goes to show that you can't keep a good man down!
I think I'll wait here! The next person to come along this path is mine!! *(He hears someone coming)* And who's this?
You see? I was right! You don't have to wait too long in this game before someone offers themselves up as my prey! *(Rubs hands together in anticipation. Enter Red. Sees wolf and slows down)*

Red: Good day!

Wolf: And good day to you, Madam!

Red: Miss!

Wolf: Not if I can help it!

Red: Sorry?

Wolf: No need to be! *(looks her up and down)* My, you are a pretty girl, aren't you! And what a lovely cloak! *(to audience)* I like my food "ready-wrapped!" *(to Red)* Yes, you are a picture!

Red: Why thank you!

Wolf: Yes, good enough to eat!

Red: What?

Wolf: Metaphorically speaking, of course! You don't believe I'd hurt you, do you?

Red: Well....!

Wolf: How could you think so badly of me? We've only just met!
Let's ask this lot, shall we? *(to audience)* I wouldn't hurt her, would I? Oh no I wouldn't! Ssshhh! You'll give me away!

Red:	My mum said that I'm not to talk to strangers!
Wolf:	*(a bit annoyed)* How very wise!
Red:	And anyway, the children would warn me if someone came up behind me, *(to audience)* wouldn't you?
Wolf:	*(glares at audience)* So there ARE children here! How nice!
Red:	So, I'll bid you good day, and I'll be off!
Wolf:	Yes, of course! Er, would you like some sweets to eat on your way?
Red:	Sweets?
Wolf:	Yes! Lovely, sticky sweets!
Red:	They're bad for my teeth!
Wolf:	Yes, but one or two won't hurt! There's a bag down behind that tree!
Red:	Where? *(bends down)* Down here? *(wolf starts to creep up on her. Audience shouts. Red gets up quickly)* What was that?
Wolf:	Er, it was a huge bee! I swatted it away!
Red:	Thank you! Look, I won't have a sweet! I'm not allowed to accept gifts off strangers!
Wolf:	Quite right! Well, before you go, you must see my puppy!
Red:	You have a puppy?
Wolf:	Yes! He is an adorable little thing! If you sit just here and shout for him, he'll come!
Red:	*(sits down)* What's his name?
Wolf:	Er, Eat me!
Red:	"Eat me?" That's a funny name for a puppy!
Wolf:	Yes, he's a strange dog! His father was a chihuahua and his mother was a great dane!
Red:	Very well! Eat me! Eat me! Come on Eat me!
Wolf:	If you insist! *(starts to pounce. Audience shouts. To audience)* I was only doing what she said!
Red:	*(gets up)* What happened then?
Wolf:	*(indicates to audience)* It's that lot out there! They're playing tricks on you!
Red:	I don't think so!
Wolf:	Well, they're getting my hackles up!
Red:	I must go! I've got to get this food to grandma's!
Wolf:	Food? Grandma?
Red:	Yes?
Wolf:	Wait a minute! Young, juicy girl, frail but mature grandma, and food??
Red:	Yes?
Wolf:	*(yells with glee)* Jackpot!! *(talks to stomach)* Bear with me, belly! We'll be back soon! *(steps forward to audience)* If I play this very carefully, I could have her, her gran and the basket of food! A three course meal!! What a feast! But first I must hold her up, to give me a chance to lay my trap! *(turns back to Red)* My dear girl, you look so tired! How much further do you have to go?
Red:	Well, I am rather tired, and grandma's is at the end of the path, right out of these woods!
Wolf:	Why don't you rest a while! Have a bit of fun?
Red:	Well, the path of truth can be tiring but it's worth it in the end!

Wolf: But wouldn't you like to play?

Red: Play? Where?

Wolf: *(points into trees)* Just inside, in a clearing there is a funfair!

Red: You have a funfair?

Wolf: Why yes!! There's roundabouts and helter skelters, roller coasters and carousels, candy floss and ice creams. It's all free! If you listen, you can hear the other children enjoying themselves!

Red: *(listens hard)* I can't hear anything!

Wolf: Well I can, but then I can hear everything people say! You must go closer! Why don't you just pop in and take a peek!

Red: I'd like to, but mum said I wasn't to stop!

Wolf: But you're not really stopping, are you! You're just taking a detour! You'll have so much fun! And the path is only here! You'll find it again, no problem!

Red: *(starts to edge into woods)* What? Just in here?

Wolf: A few more steps and you'll hear the music!

Red: In the clearing?

Wolf: That's it! Keep going! It's just ahead! You can't miss it!
(Red enters wood and has gone. Wolf jumps up and down with excitement) Yes! Yes! That'll take care of her for a while! Now, I must dash to grandma's cottage. The dear sweet old lady, boy is she in for a surprise! But, don't worry children! I haven't forgotten about you! For as a wise man once said, "I'll be back!!!" Ha! Ha! Ha!

(Exit wolf)

END OF SCENE

ACT ONE - SCENE FIVE

Scene: Grandma's cottage. A tired wolf appears.

Wolf: This must be it! Phew! It's taken me longer than I thought!
I'm not able to walk on the path of truth, so I had to stay on the outskirts of the wood. The "grey areas" I call them! That's where the truth and deception come really close! But now I'm here, I'll have to get in! I know! I'll knock on the door and pretend to be somebody else!

(Wolf knocks on cottage door. Gran shouts out from inside)

Gran: Who is it?

Wolf: *(puts on a voice)* Hello? It's the postman!

Gran: If it's the Jehovah's witnesses, I'm not interested!

Wolf: No, it's the postman!

Gran: Oh! I'll have two pints of gold top, please!

Wolf: *(shouts louder)* No, it's the postman! Postman!!

Gran: Toast pan? What's a toast pan? If you're a peddler selling, I'm not buying!

Wolf: No! It's the post man! I've got some letters for you but I'm having trouble raising the flap!

Gran: What the flap??

Wolf: TROUBLE RAISING THE FLAP!

Gran: Double glazing?

Wolf: *(in desperation)* No!!

Gran: I don't want double glazing! Go away!

Wolf: Not double glazing! *(decides to change tack)* Okay, look! I'm the milkman!

Gran: Who?

Wolf: The milkman!

Gran: Just post the letters through the flap!

Wolf: No! The milkman! I've brought you double milk!

Gran: Trouble at mill? What do you mean "trouble at mill?" If there's trouble, you'd better call the police!

Wolf: Aha! Now I have her! *(knocks on door)*

Gran: Who is it?

Wolf: It's the police!

Gran: They want you up the mill!

Wolf: *(to audience)* Right! I'll have to change my plan of attack!
I know, I'll tell her that her house is on fire! She'll have to come out then! *(knocks on door)*

Gran: Who is it?

Wolf: It's the fire department!

Gran: The fire department?

Wolf: *(to audience)* She heard me! *(shouts)* Yes!!

Gran: What's the matter?

Wolf: You'll have to come out! Your house is on fire!

Gran: My house is on fire? How did that happen?

Wolf: *(getting impatient)* For heaven's sake! Er, the farmer lit a fire in his field and it's spread too far!!

Gran: Why did the farmer light a fire in his field?

Wolf: I don't know! Oh, he was blazing some stubble!

Gran: He was what?

Wolf: *(shouts louder)* Stubble blazing!

Gran: Double glazing? You lot don't give up, do you! I don't want double glazing! Go away!

Wolf: *(gets angry)* Look Granny, you'd better open this door, or else!

Gran: Or else what?

Wolf: Er, or else you're in deep trouble!

Gran: Oh yeah? From who?

Wolf: Me!

Gran: You and who's army?

Wolf: I'll let all hell break loose! *(gran blows raspberry)* Look, open this door, or I'll huff and I'll puff and I'll blow your house down!

Gran: Try it!

Wolf: *(looks hopelessly at door)* Well, it worked on the three little pigs! If it was a Barratt house, I might have a chance! It's no use! I'm not going to get in this way!
So, I'll have to get her to come out! *(knocks twice)*

Gran: Who's there?

Wolf: Eva!

Gran: Eva who?

Wolf: Eva you open the door, or your grand-daughter goes tonsil diving!

Gran: Red? Is that you?

Wolf: *(in high voice)* Oh help Grandma! He's going to eat me!
He's licking his lovely lips and grinning a knockout smile! Strong, muscular, fit, handsome!

Gran: What?

Wolf: *(snaps back to senses)* I mean, he's leering at me while holding me with his grubby little paws! Help!!

Gran: Hold on darling! Grandma's coming!
(sounds of numerous locks being opened. Wolf stands close in anticipation. Door opens and enter granny with head band and judo costume.)
Ah ha!!
(notices there's no sign of Red) Where's my grand-daughter?
(wolf laughs) Why, you wicked creature! Now you'll pay for this!

Wolf: *(feeling confident)* Oh yeah! How come?

Gran: I am a tenth dan in origami! And a black belt in the ancient art of Ty-phoo!

Wolf: What's that?

Gran: It's the same as Kung fu but weaker! Hi yah!

Wolf: *(yawns)* Knock it off granny! Let's get it over with! *(He goes to grab her but she kicks him flying)*

Gran: I really enjoy this! It's one way to keep the wolf from your door!

Wolf: *(getting up)* I get a kick out of it too!

Gran: Do you want another?

Wolf: *(Staggering)* Wait! Wait! Before we go on, shouldn't we face each other and bow, out of respect?

Gran: I'm game!

(They face each other and bow together, but because they stand too close to each other, they crack heads. Gran slumps to the ground, out cold. Wolf is dazed with a sore head)

Wolf: Ow, ow, ow! She's a hardnut! Thankfully, my head's harder!
That'll teach her to go head to head with me! Trouble is, I've got a headache now, and my stomach feels queasy after that kick! I really can't face a meal right now! I know, I'll stick her in a cupboard for later! *(drags granny off, re-appears)* Now, all I have to do is find a clean night gown. I'll dress up as granny and jump into her bed. After a little nap, I'll be ready! And when Red comes, I'll pounce on her! Ha! Ha! Whammo! Oh my head! I must dash, because lunch is coming and there's so much to do!
Ha! Ha!
(Wolf exits)

END OF SCENE AND ACT ONE.

ACT TWO - SCENE ONE

Scene: Red roams lost in the wood. Music starts and she sings.

"NO COMPROMISE!"

Sitting alone in the dark of the woods,
I sift my way through the events of today,
thinking of how I'd have handled things better,
how differently things would have turned out that way.
I've gone the road that I said I wouldn't,
your path for me lies up another way!

All of my trials are inconsequential,
when they are compared on the grand scale of things.
To strengthen my guard would be preferential,
To remain in your will. Temptation stings!
All I want is to be in your favour,
All I want is to be with the King of Kings.

Lord, sometimes your path can be a lonely road,
'specially when friends go a different way.
But who was with you when they hit the nails,
when you bore the price that was ours to pay!

In this place, wisdom spirals to madness
and all your standards crumble to dust.
Forgive me Lord and guide my steps,
for by your Word, in you I can trust.
You're the one who'll secure my freedom,
Jesus Christ, the Name above all Names.

Lord, sometimes your path can be a lonely road,
'specially when friends go a different way,
but who was with you when they hit the nails,
when you bore the price that was ours to pay!

Now as I feel that all is against me,
I feel your touch as you're by my side.
Your Word is a lamp, a light that guides me.
Your love and mercy cannot be denied.
With all my strength I'll stand by your values,
from now on, there'll be no compromise!

(Song ends)

Red: Hey! It's a bit lighter now! Thank you Lord. It was really scary earlier, but at least I can see where I'm going.
He path
That wicked wolf has tricked me into here and I can't find my way back to the path. Wait a minute! I can hear voices. If I find them, maybe they can tell me how to get back!
Then again, they might not be friendly. Oh, I don't know what to do!

(Suddenly, the curtains open to reveal a game show set. Red stands aside and watches the proceedings. There is a host on one side and three 'panelists' on the other)

Troy: Hi! I'm Troy Smilee, and welcome to another game of "What's My Deception!" *(drum roll and smash)* Thank you Floyd!
Let's meet the panel.
First, the man that's done for English what the guillotine did for sore throats. There isn't anything that I wouldn't do for him and there isn't anything he wouldn't do for me.
That's why we've gone through life not doing anything for each other. I mean, of course, the eminent pschotherapiologist, Dr. Gustav Ludwig Von Smorgersborg!

Gus: Thank you Troy!

Troy: And sitting beside him, a woman who needs no introduction, because she hasn't turned up! So instead, please welcome the queen of sleaze, Tanya Bottom!

Tanya: Ohh, you tinker!

Troy: And last and definitely least, a marvellous, talented and funny man (well, that's what it says here!) my script writer, Spurgeon McKlondyke!

Spur: Hi! I'm Troy Smilee!

Troy: Right! You all know the rules, so it's on with the game!
Will our first contestant please sign in!

(Enter man with neck in collar and arm in plaster. Signs with mouth)

Troy: Okay! For those of you who can't read that, this is Olaf Lufthasen! Hello Olaf! *(Olaf nods)* Now then panel, it's time to put your headphones on! *(They do so)* As our panel enjoys some music, Olaf will tell us what his deception is! Olaf?

Olaf: I thought I could fly!

Troy: Thank you Olaf! *(thumbs up to panel)* Right, we're ready panel. Who's going to begin?

Gus: I will, Troy!

Troy: Thank you Gustav.

Gus: Hello Olaf.

Olaf: Hello!

Gus: Olaf, is your deception a cinto psycho cerebro malingo social problem?

(Troy and Olaf look at one another)

Troy: No, it's not! *(puts up 1 on pad)* That's one wrong!

Gus: Does it involve other people?

Olaf: Only if they get in the way!

Troy: So that's no! *(puts up 2)* Tanya?

Tanya: Yes, hello Olaf! Is it contagious? Could we all be deceived this way?

Troy: Er, no! Not really! I think this is Olaf's personal baby! *(turns up 3)*

Tanya: Er, um, Oh, I don't know! Oh, Have your injuries come about as a result of your deception?

Olaf: Yes!

Troy: Now we're getting somewhere!

Tanya: *(getting excited)* I know! I know!

Troy: I'm sorry Tanya! It's Spurgeon's go!

Spur: Hi! I'm Troy Smilee!

Troy: Thank you Spurgeon! Now I'll open it out to the others!

Gus: I know!

Tanya: I know!!

Troy: Gustav?

Gus: As a result of a trauma in your early years, you think that you're a chicken!

Troy: No! *(up goes 4)* Tanya?

Tanya: You think you're Bruce Lee?

Troy: No, I'm afraid not! *(up goes 5)* Spurgeon?

Spur: Hi! I'm Troy Smilee?

Troy: No, wrong again! And that's all your guesses! *(up goes 6)*

Panel: What was it?
Troy: He thought that he could fly!

Panel: Oh, of course!

Troy: Congratulations Olaf! Here's your trophy and thank you for playing! *(Olaf exits to much applause)* Will the next guest please sign in!

(A huge gong sounds and a genie enters. His name appears miraculously on the paper)

Troy: Right panel! This is Mr Genie from Lamp! Hello Mr Genie! *(Genie nods)* Headphones on please! Mr Genie, your deception please!

Genie: I am the genie of the lamp! I have come to grant you a wish!

Troy: Well maybe later, but now we need to know...er..

Genie: *(suddenly realising)* Oh yes, I'm sorry! I keep thinking this pantomime is "Aladdin!"

Troy: I see, thank you! Now, when the panel's ready, we'll begin! Er, Tanya first, I think!

Tanya: Thank you! Do you grant wishes?

Troy: Yes he does, but your questions must be more direct!

Tanya: Okay! Er, d'yah think you could make my nose smaller, and give me a face lift and tummy tuck?

Troy: I think that's a no! *(turns 1)* Spurgeon?

Spur: Hi! I'm Troy Smilee?

Troy: Thank you! (2) And Gustav!

Gus: Thank you! Hello Genie! Tell me, did your parents ever lock you in a small bottle when you were little?

Genie: *(sadly)* Yes!

Troy: Good question Gustav!

Gus: And do you have nightmares?

Troy: Er, I'll have to give a "no!" for that! (3) Not getting to the point, I think! Tanya?

Tanya: Yeah, a guy like you could be useful! Are you looking for someone to be with?

Genie: Yes I am!

Troy: That's a yes, but we're not....

Genie: I'm looking for Aladdin!

Troy: Oh, now see! You've told them!

Panel: Of course! He thinks he's in Aladdin!

Troy: I'm sorry Mr Genie but this game's over for you! Goodbye! Give him a nice round of applause! *(genie exits to sad music)* Now, to our last guest. This, of course is the mystery deception round and so the person will not reveal it to the audience until the panel does! All clear? Then we'll continue. Mystery guest, please sign in! *(woman walks in and signs)* Hello Agnes Ostic and welcome to the show!

Agnes: Thank you!

Troy: How long have you had this deception?

Agnes: Since I was born!

Troy: I see! So, there you are Panel! Fire away!

Gus: Hello Agnes! Tell me, does this deception bother you at all?

Agnes: No! Except when people I know and loved ones die!

Troy: So Agnes, is that a "yes" or "no?"

Agnes: Well, yes, I suppose!

Troy: Thank you! Next question Gustav!
Gus: Thank you! Er, Agnes, do you sometimes feel lonely and isolated, as if nobody loves you and you are worthless?

Agnes: Er, yes, I suppose so! But I've got to remain true to my logic! Without logic, where are we?

Gus: Well, you've got logic and you're still stuck in here!

Troy: Thank you Gustav! Another yes! Two good questions from him! Tanya?

Tanya: Er, yes! Er, do you feel like I do sometimes that your life is out of control?

Agnes: Er yes! Constantly! But I'm just going through a very rough time at the moment!

Troy: How long has it lasted?

Agnes: Oh, since my teens!

Troy: That's a long time! Good question Tanya!

Tanya: Um! Right! Do you feel you've got all the answers?

Agnes: No!

Troy: Our first no! *(turns 1)*

Gus: I've got it!

Troy: One moment Gustav! It's Spurgeon's turn!

Spur: Hi! I'm Troy Smilee!

Troy: Thank you Spurgeon! Now then, Gustav believes he has it!   Gustav?

Gus: Do you believe that you can get through life easily without God?

Troy: Agnes?

Agnes: Yes, that's it! Well done!

Troy: Well done Gustav! *(panel congratulates Gus)* So Agnes, why do you have this deception?

Agnes: Well, I don't know really! I'm just not interested in all that church stuff. And anyway, lots of people make it through life without God!

Troy: And after life?

Agnes: *(looks worried)* I really don't know!

Troy: Well, thank you Agnes, and I hope you enjoyed yourself on the show!

> *(Red light shines in corner of stage with smoke rising out of it.*
> *A little demon awaits Agnes as she rises from her seat)*

Agnes: Thank you! I did!

Troy: And all the best with where you're going! Give her a big hand!
(huge applause as Agnes is grabbed by demon and carted off into red mist.)
And I hope that you've enjoyed the show! My thanks go to the panel, chaired by, Dr. Smogersborg!

Gus: Goodnight!

Troy: Tanya Bottom!

Tanya: (winks) See yah!

Troy: And my old mate, Spurgeon McKlondyke!

Spur: Hi! I'm Troy Smilee!

Troy: And who knows? Next time, it could be you on the show! So, until then, from all of us on "What's My Deception?", it's Goodnight!

> *(Music starts and fades, curtains close and Red is left standing all alone and very puzzled)*

Red: This is a very strange place!!

END OF SCENE.

29

ACT TWO - SCENE TWO

Scene: Red walks uneasily through the wood, and hears a creature moving ahead!

Red: Hello? Who's there?

Crtr1: Don't hurt me! Don't hurt me!

Red: Who are you? Come out where I can see you!

Crtr1: *(appears, limping)* Please! Don't hurt me! I'm sorry to bother you, but I'm lame and I was wondering if you could find it in your heart to spare me a few coppers! I'm not worth your consideration, I know, but it would help!

Red: Of course, but you shouldn't be too hard on yourself! Just because you're lame doesn't mean you're nothing! And you must be more positive! There's worse things than being lame! You could be blind!

Crtr1: You're right!

Red: Good!

Crtr1: When I was blind, people kept giving me Monopoly money!

(He walks away, limping on other leg)

Red: Wait a minute! What do you mean, "When I was blind?" And you're limping on the wrong leg! You're a fraud!

Crtr1: *(Instantly remorseful)* You're right!

Red: You should be ashamed of yourself, pretending to be lame and tricking me like that! A disability is a serious thing and you should be glad you're healthy, not using it to con people!

Crtr1: I'm sorry! I am the lowest of the low! A snake! Nay, lower than a snake! An ant! No, a worm!

Red: Steady on!

Crtr1: No, you're right! I am worthless! Once, someone saved my life and I rewarded them with fifty pence. They gave me forty five pence change!!

Red: Oh, come on! It's not that bad!

Crtr1: You don't know! I'm beyond redemption! I once bet £10 on a football match - and lost! I bet another £10 on the instant replay - and lost again!!

Red: You must be good at something?

Crtr1: Well, I have invented things!

Red: Oh, how clever!

Crtr1: Not really! They never caught on!

Red: Why?

Crtr1: Not much call for an ejector seat in a helicopter! Nor a parachute that opens on impact!

Red: Oh dear! *(tries to change subject)* Don't you have any friends?

Crtr1: People don't like me!

Red: Surely not?

Crtr1: They don't! I used to play rugby! Every time they went down for a scrum, I used to think they were talking about me!

Red: No?

Crtr1: I once tried to hire a room with a Muslim and a Jew, but there were only two beds, so someone had to sleep in the barn! The Muslim volunteered and off he went! Five minutes later, there was a knock on the door. It was the Muslim! Apparently, there was a cow in the barn and it was against his religion to sleep with a cow! So, the Jew said he'd sleep in the barn! But five minutes later, there was a knock on the door. It was the Jew! He said there was a pig in the barn and it was against his religion to sleep with a pig! So, I said I'd sleep in the barn, and off I went!
Five minutes later, there was a knock on the door! It was the pig and the cow!

Red: Okay, okay! That's sad! But you won't endear yourself to anyone by feigning an injury!

Crtr1: Oh I don't know! I think injuries are good for you!

Red: How do you work that out?

Crtr1: Well, since I cricked my neck, I've never looked back!

Red: Why not?

Crtr1: I haven't been able to!

Red: Oh! So, you have survived here! It seems an awful place!

Crtr1: Well, when I'm feeling peckish or really hungry,
I'll fry a drop of hedgehog snot and have it for my tea!
I'll wash it down with slug slime, mixed with crunchy dirt then I'll get some rabbit droppings and have them for dessert!

Red: Urgh! That's disgusting!

Crtr1: If you think that's bad, the coffee here tastes like mud!

Red: That's awful!

Crtr1: Well, it was GROUND this morning!!

Red: Very funny!

Crtr1: It wasn't supposed to be! See! I even got that wrong!

Red: Wait a minute? I recognise you!

Crtr1: *(trying to hide face in shame)* No you don't! You can't!

Red: Yes I do! You're one of the travellers who came to my birthday party!

Crtr1: You must be mistaken!

Red: Yes you are! Hey, don't worry! What's wrong?

Crtr1: It's..... it's just that I'm ashamed!

Red: Ashamed? Ashamed of what?

Crtr1: Of what I am! Of what I've become! That you should see me now!

Red: What happened to you? Why are you in these woods? What happened to the Word I gave you?

Crtr1: The Word? Oh, I was so blessed by that word! But as we travelled along the path after taking your grandmother home, I stopped to rest a while! The others went on, thinking I'd catch up. But the wolf jumped out of the trees at me!

Red: The wolf?

Crtr1: Yes! He stole the word from me and gave me a piece of paper. On it was a riddle! He told me that I must solve the riddle to escape from the wood! Then he chased me and I ran, deeper and deeper into the trees, trying to get away! And here I am!

Red: What does the riddle say?

Crtr1: Here! *(takes paper out of pocket and gives to Red)* You read it! I can't bear it!

Red: *(reads)* "You are the worm, the lowest of low, you know not where to turn or which way to go! Answer to the One who destined your birth, then you'll discover your value and worth!"

Crtr1: You see?

Red: No wonder you don't think much of yourself!

Crtr1: But it's true!

Red: No it's not, and I'm going to prove it!!

Crtr1: How?

Red: By solving your riddle, with the Lord's help!

Crtr1: How are you going to do that?

Red: Well, you are trapped! And the knowledge of the truth shall set you free! I have the truth, the Word of God, and it declares that "The unfolding of the Word gives light and understanding!"

Crtr1: Well, please try!

Red: Well, the riddle says you're worthless, but the Word says, "If anyone loves me, he will obey my teaching! My Father will love him, and We will come to him and make Our home with him!" Wow! Imagine having the Father and Jesus living with you?

Crtr1: They wouldn't want to live with me, would they?

Red: You heard the Word! It goes on, "Whoever does the will of my Father in heaven is my Brother!" Oh ho!! Now you're a relative!

Crtr1: But why would Jesus want a low-life like me for a brother?

Red: Let's see, shall we? It also says, "Now if you obey me fully and keep my covenant, then out of all nations, you will be my treasured possession!" You're not a low-life! You're a treasured possession!

Crtr1: *(straightening up)* I am?

Red: Yes, but there seems to be a key to it all! Your riddle says, "Answer to the one who destined your birth!" Well, that's God, who destines all births! He knew us all before we were born! So you must answer to Him, or rather "OBEY!"
That's the key! You can leave this place of deception by obeying God!

Crtr1: *(becomes more human)* You're right! I will obey the Lord my God! *(light shines brightly on him)* Wow? What's happening?

Red: *(smiling)* You've been released from your deception! You're free to rejoin the path of truth!

Crtr1: Thank you for everything!

Red: The pleasure's all mine!

(The creature leaves and Red continues in the woods, off stage)

END OF SCENE.

ACT TWO - SCENE THREE

Scene: Four creatures sat around long table, different items in front of each

Leader: (stands) Okay, order! Order! I'd just like to begin the second monthly meeting of the "New Order of Spiritual Environmental Worship, Idols and Paranormal Energy Society!"

Othrs: Here, here!

Lder: Will you all please be upstanding for the national anthem!
(encourages audience to join in. Creatures stand)

All: Woo woo whippy woo, nibble snipe dong,
Wabba wabba zing bock, arooga arooga pong,
Zim zim ploopa, he he phlegm,
Yak yak (wobble throat) Eyeee, (cough) Amen!

Lder: And now the reciting of the creed. "I believe and worship our idols above all else...."

Othrs: Hallelujah!

Lder: "...I will never brush my teeth...."

Othrs: Halitosis!

Lder: "...and wait for the coming of the great rock in the sky!"

Othrs: Halley's comet!

Lder: Amen!

Othrs: Amen!

Lder: Now, before we start, has anyone got anything they'd like to say?

No.2: Yes!

Lder: What?

No.2: Our name!

Lder: What about it?

No.2: The "New Order of Spiritual Environment Worship, Idols and Paranormal Energy Society!"

Lder: Yeah?

No.2: Do you know what the initials spell?

Lder: Of course I do! Your point being?

No.2: It spells Nosewipes!

Lder: So?

No.2: Let's change the name!

Lder: Why?

No.2: I don't wanna be a Nosewipe!

No.4: Too late if you ask me!

No.2: Well I'm not asking you! I'm asking him!

Lder: Listen brother, you objected to the other names put forward!

No.2: Yeah! The "Creators of Radical Energy Through Individual Notion Society?"

Lder: Yeah! What was wrong with that?

No.2: CRETINS? (The others think he's calling them names and get upset) No! It spells Cretins!

No.3: Well, what about my idea! The "People's Republic of Astute Thinkers!"

No.2: None of us wanted to be a PRAT!

Lder: Well reminded! But the point is that until someone comes up with a better name, you're a Nosewipe, I'm a Nosewipe and they're Nosewipes too! Okay?

No.3: SNOT a good name! Geddit?

Lder: *(ignoring last statement)* So, we'll get on! Right, let's see what idols we have today! No.2, what have you got there?

No.2: *(gets excited)* Aha! What I have here is one of the most potent forces in the universe!

No.4: Oh no! You haven't been eating pickled eggs again, have you?

No.2: *(gets defensive)* No! It's this! *(uncovers a crystal)*

All: Wow! Ooooh! Ahh! *(Silence)*

Lder: *(after a pause)* What is it?

No.2: It's a crystal, innit?

Lder: A crystal what?

No.2: A crystal nuffink! Just a crystal!

Lder: What? Just a crystal?

No.2: Yes!

Lder: Well, that's a load of rubbish! Next!

No.2: Hold on! This is very powerful!

Lder: 'Ow d'you mean?

No.2: Well, it sucks the energy and vibes from the universe and focuses it wherever you want it!

Lder: It what?

No.2: Sucks energy!

Lder: What? Is it sucking now?

No.2: Yeah!

Lder: *(gets closer and listens)* Well I can't hear anything!
Shouldn't it go... *(makes a sucking noise)*

No.2: Nah nah! I will demonstrate!

Lder: Please do!

No.2: I will tune it in with the universe! Hold on! *(sound of radio tuning, followed by jingle and voice of D.J. Then it stops and No.2 looks pleased with himself)* You see!

Lder: *(looks at others who are puzzled)* What was that?

No.2: I got in touch with the Spirit King, ...! *(Name of D.J.)*

Lder: *(shakes his head)* I'll need a bit more convincing before I go with that one! Next!

No.3: *(reads from book)* "Next" meaning nearest, soonest come to, first ensuing, immediately following or proceeding, nearest in order!

Lder: Eh?

No.3: It's knowledge and wisdom, brother! I got it from the Good book!

Lder: What's that?

No.3: The Oxford Dictionary! Changed my life, it has! The intelligence in here has transformed my thinking! I am a new man!

Lder: Oh yeah? Who are you now then?

No.3: I am the "Wordfinder General!"

Lder: Oh!

No.3: I will demonstrate the power of this book!

Lder:	*(confused)* That'll be nice!
No.3:	"Nice," agreeable, well-favoured, kind, friendly, considerate, satisfactory....
Lder:	Er, thank you, brother! That will be all!
No.3:	"All," the whole amount, extent or number....
Lder:	That's enough!
No.3:	"Enough," as much or many as necessary!
Lder:	*(picks up his own rock idol in a threatening manner)* Do you know what "fractured" and "skull" means?
No.3:	Yes! *(he gets the message)*
Lder:	*(puts down rock)* No.4? Would you like to demonstrate what you have?
No.4:	Certainly! I have a spirit guide! I will introduce him to you! First, I must get in a trance, for the fluance, you understand!
Lder:	Of course, the fluance!
No.4:	*(starts rocking side to side)* Is there anybody there? Knock once for "yes" and twice for "no!" *(one knock)*
No.2:	He did that with his foot!
Lder:	Shush! You'll disturb the fluance!
No.2:	The grotty Nosewipe!
Lder:	Shut it!
No.4:	There's somebody there! It's my spirit guide! Hello! Please make yourself visible! *(lifts hand to reveal SOOTY hand puppet! Sooty whispers into No. 4's ear)* Is there anybody here called "Sweep?"
Othrs:	*(looking very puzzled)* No!
No.3:	"Sweep," to gather up or collect, clear away....
Lder:	Shush!!
No.4:	Well, "Sue" then?
Othrs:	No!
No.4:	*(out of trance)* Well what about "Matthew" or "Scampy?"
Lder:	Oh, this is ridiculous!
No.4:	Oh yeah? You've been so busy ridiculing our idols, what have you got then? *(others nod and agree)*
Lder:	Watch it! Watch it! *(points to rock with eyes painted on it)* This is the great god Bejam, Lord of supermarkets! If you don't watch out, he'll turn you into consumer products!
No.2:	It's just a rock with eyes painted on it!
Lder:	Eh? Blasphemer! Bejam the almighty has awesome power!
No.2:	Oh yeah?
Lder:	Yeah! And he desires lots of sacrifices to be made unto him! Why, only yesterday, he devoured a bunch of cows!
No.3:	*No, herd!*
Lder:	Eh?
No.3:	Herd!
Lder:	Heard of what?

No.3: Herd of cows!

Lder: Of course I've heard of cows!

No.3: No! A cow herd!

Lder: I don't care if a cow heard! I've got no secrets from a cow!

No.4: Wait! Wait! I'm getting a message! The spirit guide is giving me an incantation! It goes, "Izzy wizzy, let's get busy!"

All: Izzy wizzy let's get busy!

Lder: Well that didn't do anything!

No.2: Wait! The crystal's sucking more energy! *(more radio noise, then part of a song by Des O'Connor)*

Lder: Turn it off!

Othrs: Turn it off!!

Lder: Turn it off!!! It's possessed!

No.3: "Possessed," mad, to be foolish, or inhabited by!

Lder: You're getting right up my nose!

No.2: I told you he was a Nosewipe!

Lder: Look! Will every one just stop!!

(Enter Red)

Red: Hello?

Lder: Oh, hello! Help at last! Please join us!

Red: Why, are you coming apart?

Lder: Sorry?

Red: Oh, nothing! *(sits down)*

Lder: Now then, my dear! What have you brought us?

Red: I'm sorry?

Lder: To the meeting! Your contribution!

No.3: "Contribution," payment made or thing given or done in aid of a....!

Lder: You are seriously in danger of suffering a fatal accident!

No.3: *(sheepishly)* Sorry!

Red: What do you mean, my contribution?

Lder: To the meeting! Show us your idol!

Red: I don't have an idol!

Lder: Do you hear that, lads? She doesn't have an idol! *(They all laugh)*
My dear, you must have something to guide and protect you?

Red: Oh, I have that!

Lder: Good! Let's see it then! *(Red gets out Bible)* What's that then?

Red: That's the living Word of God!

Lder: Well I can't hear it breathing!

Red: But it breathes life into situations!

Lder: Nah! Rubbish! It's useless!

Red: No it's not!

Lder: Yes it is! What we've got's more powerful than that!

Red: Okay! A contest! I'll pit my Bible against any of your idols!

Lder: Okay! D'yah hear that, lads? A wager! This'll be easy! Power 'em up!

Red: Right! Who's first!

No.2: I'll go first! This crystal's power will destroy you!
  (There's just a lot of radio static)

Red: The Word says, "You shall not make for yourself an idol in the form of anything in heaven above or on the earth beneath, or in the waters below!"

No.3: Okay then! I'll test your book against my book!

Red: Well, mine's called "The Holy Bible."

No.3: Then I'll use the knowledge and wisdom contained in these pages to blast your book to pieces! Let's see, Holy! Here we are! "Holy," belonging or devoted to God! And "Bible," authoritative text book!

Red: So, it's an authoritative text book devoted to God!

No.3: Ooops!

Red: My book says, "Since we are God's offspring, we should not think that the Divine being is like gold or silver or stone, an image made by man's design and skill!"

No.3: What's happened? This book makes no sense to me anymore!

Red: "I will destroy the wisdom of the wise, the intelligence of the intelligent I will frustrate! Has not God made foolish the wisdom of this world?"

No.4: *(listens to sooty)* Izzy wizzy, let's get busy??

Red: "The Holy Spirit clearly states that in latter times, some will abandon their faith and follow deceiving spirits and things taught by demons!"

Lder: You have done well, but now it ends! You will never defeat the power of Bejam's stare! Prepare to meet your doom!

Red: "Do not make idols or set up an image or a sacred stone for yourselves, and do not place a carved stone in your land to bow before it. I am the Lord your God!"
  (Bejam keels over)

Lder: What's happened? Why weren't you afraid?

Red: The Word says, "Like a scarecrow in a melon patch, their idols cannot speak; they must be carried because they cannot walk. Do not fear them; they can do no harm, nor can they do any good!!

Lder: That is truly a powerful book! We have lost!

Red: YOU haven't lost! Just the forces that bid to hold you captive! You are some of the travellers! What happened to the word I gave you?

Lder: We received it with joy and went on our journey...

No.2: ...but we heard the wolf coming...

No.3: ...and we dropped it...

No.4: ...and ran away...

Lder: ...and when we got here, we found a riddle! We thought it was telling us how to protect ourselves in future! We really need something that's powerful enough to help us!

Red: Don't you know that "only perfect love casts out fear?"
  And "the Lord preserves the faithful!" Let me see your riddle!
  (No.3 gives it to her. She reads)
  "The first is in tarot and also in cards,
  The second is in evil that protects and guards,

The third is in people, the wisest of wise,
The fourth is in power you see with your eyes,
The fifth is in demon but never in day,
The sixth is in stone to worship and pray.
Take heed of these things, this must be understood,
You must do this to escape from the wood!"

Lder: You see! It was telling us what to do!

Red: Take heed can mean watch out or beware! It was warning you of these things! No, to solve this one, you must take a letter out of each line to make up a word! Let's see!
That's R, E, P, E, N and T! REPENT! That's what you lot must do to get out of the woods!

Lder: You're right!

Othrs: Yes, yes!

Red: Well now's as good a time as any!

All: *(They all hug together)* Dear God, we are so sorry!
Please forgive us our foolishness. We will do as you say!

(Suddenly, they all straighten up and become human again)

Lder: Hey, that's wonderful!!

No.3: Brilliant! Fantastic! Words fail me!

No.4: I just want to get busy for God! Thank you!

Red: That's alright!

No.2: Does this mean we're not Nosewipes anymore!

Red: That's right! Now, you can say you're the "Society of Added Valour, by Encouragement and Direction!"

All: *(They work it out)* Oh, SAVED!

Red: Yes!

Lder: Thank you! We must go and find our way home! Will you come with us?

Red: I'd love to, but we've all got to find our own way through these woods! I hope I'll meet you soon, though!

Lder: Us too! Well, goodbye!

All: Goodbye!

Red: Goodbye, and God bless!

(They exit one way and Red exits another)

END OF SCENE.

ACT TWO - SCENE FOUR

Scene: *Red walks boldly through the wood. Then she hears and sees something moving ahead.*

Red: Hello? *(no answer)* Hello? Don't be scared! *(still no answer)* Come on! Maybe I can help you!
Look! *(holds out Bible)* I have the Word of the Lord here! Come and see!
(A deep growl emerges from the darkness. Red is afraid!)
I won't hurt you! I want to help you! *(growling gets louder)* Please don't! You're frightening me!
(It doesn't stop) I only want to help!

(Suddenly, creature 6 leaps out of dark and tears the Bible out of Red's hands! She is plunged into darkness. The creature circles her, laughing menacingly)

Crtr6:   Now I have you!

Red: Please! I don't want to hurt you! Please don't hurt me!

Crtr6:   Now we're equal, both in the dark! Except that I can see you! Ha! Ha!

Red: *(very afraid)* Oh Lord, please help me! Your Word was my light and it's gone!!

(Sings "Your Words are written on my heart!" When she reaches first chorus, it grows lighter again, confusing creature)

"YOUR WORDS ARE WRITTEN ON MY HEART!"

Caught out in the dark, I've never felt so scared.
I can feel the evil closing in!
Walking round me now, I can see his sharp teeth bared,
hot breath beating on my skin, beating on my skin.

I've lost your written Word. It lies torn upon the ground,
and this creature has me in it's snare!
But as I think that there's no hope, and there's no help to be
found, I remember reading somewhere,
Words that really gave me hope in my sorrow,
Lines that burst upon my soul, today, tomorrow,

Your Words are written on my heart,
There is nothing to keep us apart.
They are a guide to lead me, a lamp that lights my way,
Living words that turn the night to day, turn the night to day!

You see the light shines brightly, you're dazzled by its glare.
Now look at what you have become!
You've grown used to the darkness, you've made your home in
there, everything but hatred leaves you numb!
Don't be scared, please draw near. It won't hurt you!
Let the darkness disappear, I won't desert you!

His words can be written on your heart,
There is nothing to keep you apart.
They are a guide to lead you, a lamp that lights your way,
Living words that turn the night to day, turn the night to day!

You can't run or fight, can't escape the light,
It's time to face the demons eating you inside.
Time to turn away, hold the dark at bay,
Time to start today, let Him light your way!

(Break for script)

Red: You! I know you!

Crtr6:   *(shrieks)* NO!!

Red: Yes! You also are one of the travellers! One of my friends!

Crtr6:   I was?

Red: Not was! ARE! You are one of my friends!

Crtr6:   It cannot be!

Red: It can, and it will be! What happened to the word I gave you?

Crtr6: The Word?

Red: Yes, the Word!

Crtr6: The Word! Yes, I had the word, *(remembering)* but the wolf...!

Red: What did the wolf do?

Crtr6: He wanted me to give him the word in exchange for riches beyond my wildest dreams!

Red: And you did?

Crtr6: Yes! But when I came into the clearing, I found no riches, only a riddle! I was so angry, I could have killed! I vowed then never to trust anyone other than myself ever again! Then I started to hate everyone and everything! *(remorseful)* And now I can't stop!

Red: Your riddle? What does it say?

Crtr6: *(gets it out)* Will you read it? I am not used to this light!

Red: *(takes it and reads)* "You trusted in money and ended up broke!
You trusted in people and started to choke!
You trust in yourself but only know hate!
This trust will destroy you, if you leave it too late!"
Is that it?

Crtr6: That's it, *(gets angry)* the cursed thing!!

Red: Now listen! We will solve it!

Crtr6: But I've destroyed your Bible!

Red: That doesn't make any difference! It's in my heart now!
And let me tell you what it says,
"Trust in the Lord and do good. Dwell in the land and enjoy safe pasture. Delight yourself in the Lord and He will give you the desires of your heart. Commit your way to the Lord; trust in Him and He will do this: He will make your righteousness shine like the dawn!"
It cannot be dark when the Lord is shining out of you!

Crtr6: It would be so good to leave this dark place! I've been here so long,
I've forgotten how refreshing light is!
(changes slightly) But I can't shake off this hate!

Red: "The only thing that counts is faith, expressing itself through love!"

Crtr6: *(starting to break down)* I want to know God more!

Red: "God is love. Whoever lives in love, lives in God, and God in him!"

Crtr6: *(drops to knees. Hate is fading)* How can I attain faithfulness in God?

Red: Again, the Word says, "The fruit of the Spirit is love, joy, peace, patience, kindness, goodness and faithfulness!" That's the key to your riddle! You must have faith in God, and trust in Him! Then you will have joy, peace and the love you so badly crave! And the way out from this wood!

(Song continues to end)
A new day's begun, started by the One,
Who's love endures for evermore.
Time to leave this place, cleansed without a trace,
By our loving King,

Who's words are written on our heart,
There is nothing to keep us apart,
They are a guide to lead us, a lamp that lights our way,
Living words that turn the night to day, turn the night to day!

(Song ends)

(Light shines to side of stage)

40

Red: Look! The deception is broken! We are free to leave!
There's nothing here to stop us anymore, and, at last,
I can see the path up ahead!

Crtr6: *(hugs Red and looks more human)* Thank you! Let's go!

Red: Yes, let's!

Crtr6: Oh, by the way?

Red: Yes?

Crtr6: Last one to the path is a rotten egg!

Red: You're on!

(Both run towards the light and exit)

END OF SCENE

ACT TWO - SCENE FIVE

Scene: Grandma's cottage. The wolf is dressed in a nightgown, hat and glasses. He waits in bed. Enter Red, outside.

Red: *(knocks on door)* Hello Gran? I'm here at last! You won't believe what's happened to me!

Wolf: *(in feeble voice)* Come in, my dear!

Red: *(rushes in)* Gran, let me tell you all about.... *(stops and looks)*... Gran! You look awful!!

Wolf: Ooh! I don't feel well at all!

Red: I know, I'm sorry! Here I am, rushing in, talking about me, me, me, and here you are - Sick! I am sorry!

Wolf: That's alright dear!

Red: Here! *(sits on bed)* Let me look at you!

Wolf: *(covers snout with blanket)* No, no! Don't come too close!
It's very infectious!

Red: Nonsense! It's only a cold!

Wolf: No, it's worse than that! The doctor said that it's developed into Wolventine Caninitus!

Red: What?

Wolf: It's a variant of puppy flu!

Red: How did you get puppy flu?

Wolf: I don't know but I'm dog-tired!

Red: Paw old you!

Wolf: You've got it!

Red: Well, I've got some lovely food for you, but I'll put it over here! You can't be feeling very hungry!

Wolf: Wanna bet?

Red: Sorry?

Wolf: Er, I said, er *(in Italian accent)* Donna let me a stop a you!

Red: Gran? Why are you talking like an Italian?

Wolf: Oh, it's this bug! It's called a Bugatti! It does that!
It makes me speak all sorts of languages. Bonjour, hola, buonos dias, bore da! See what I mean?

Red: You poor thing!

Wolf: Oui!

Red: Oh, shall I help you to the toilet?

Wolf: No! Oui, as in Yes!

Red: You Want to go to the toilet?

Wolf: No! Never mind! I'm tired out!

Red: I know! *(sits on bed again)* Let me feel your temperature!

Wolf: No!

Red: *(touches wolf's head)* Urgh! You're...you're all hairy!

Wolf: I know! My ladyshave has broken down again!

Red: Wait a minute! You look very strange, Granny!

Wolf: So would you if you had what I've got!

Red: What is it again?

Wolf: I don't know! I've forgotten!

Red: Still, it's most odd! I mean, What big ears you've got, Grandma!

Wolf: That's the doctor's fault! He pulled too hard on them when he drained off my ear wax!

Red: And what big eyes you've got, Grandma?

Wolf: Oh, that'll be my new glasses! I got one pair made within the hour at Vision Express, and a second pair absolutely free! (I'm not getting any money for this commercial, mind!)

Red: And what a big nose you've got, Grandma?

Wolf: Well, with the amount I've been sneezing, I'm surprised it's not the size of a hammerfore!

Red: What's a hammerfore?

Wolf: Knocking nails in! Ha! Ha!

Red: And your teeth?

Wolf: What about my teeth? They're not rotten, are they? I use that new Colgate with bicarbonate of soda. It's good for cooking dried peas in too! (I'm not getting anything for that commercial, either!)

Red: No, it's just... What big teeth you have, Grandma!

Wolf: Oh, all the better to eat your mother's delightful cooking, my dear!

Red: *(steps back)* Wait a minute! There's something very strange!

Wolf: What do you mean?

Red: You're not my Granny! My Granny can't stand my mum's cooking! And I think I can smell T.C.P!

Wolf: *(rips off hat and glasses)* How right you are!

Red: *(in horror)* It's you!

Wolf: Yes! *(Red tries to leave as wolf climbs out of bed)* It's no use! I've fixed the door so that you can only come in, but not go out! You're trapped! Ha! Ha!

Red: You wicked creature!

Wolf: Yes! Enjoy it in my woods, did you?

Red: No! It was horrible!

Wolf: Good! Nobody likes being deceived, but it's even worse when you can't find a way out of it! That's how I like it!

Red: I know your game!

Wolf: Oh yes? Let me tell you about myself! What big ears I have! All the better to hear the evil from Man's mouth! Then I can move in! What big eyes I have! All the better to see the wickedness and sorrow I've helped cause!
What a big nose I have! All the better to smell the fear you miserable humans have! And what big teeth I have! All the better to devour your souls when you've fallen from grace into my domain! Yes, I am fully equipped for the work in hand!

Red: I will never fall from the grace of God!

Wolf: Oh no? I thought that once, but look at me now!

Red: My God is my salvation! He will keep me from harm!

Wolf: Where is He now? I can't see Him?

Red: *(to the heavens)* Lord, please help me!

Wolf: Call to Him all you like! Maybe He'll send down a few angels, I don't care! They'd have to be quick, and besides, I have a few, er, friends who'd keep them busy for a while!

Red:	Leave me alone!
Wolf:	No! Besides, you didn't say the magic word!
Red:	Please?
Wolf:	No, but similar! Wrong word! There's only one word that can save you now! *(Suddenly, the door flies open and in step the six travellers)*
Trv.1:	Jesus!
Wolf:	*(covers ears and ducks)* Who in hades said that?
Trv.2:	In the name of Jesus, stop your wickedness here!
Wolf:	*(getting frantic)* Go away! Go away!
Red:	My friends!
Trv.3:	Hello Red! Someone bothering you?
Trv.4:	We all just felt in our Spirits that you needed us!
Trv.5:	It was as if God was telling us to find you!
Trv.6:	So we hot-legged it over here! And just in time, so it seems!
Red:	Oh, thank you Lord! And thank you, my friends! (points to wolf, cowering in corner) Now, what are we going to do with him?
Wolf:	Rarrh! Get away from me!
Trv.1:	We've got just the thing! *(to wolf)* You cursed creature! You deceived us all and trapped us with riddles! Now we have a riddle for you!
Trv.2:	My first is in Salvation that comes from above!
Trv.3:	My second's in Agape, God's gracious love!
Trv.4:	My third's in Triumph of life over death!
Trv5:	My fourth's in Adam, born by God's breath!
Trv.6:	My fifth's in Nations, bowing at Jesus's feet!
Trv.1:	My whole is Deceiver who lives in defeat! Here, take it! *(puts paper in wolf's paw)* Until you solve it, you're trapped in the woods!
All:	Now, in the name of Jesus, be gone!
Wolf:	Arghh! *(runs out and away)*
Trv.1:	We won't see him again in a hurry!
Red:	But what if he solves the riddle?
Trv.2:	He can't! The letters spell SATAN! Salvation, Agape, Triumph, Adam and Nations! If he solves it, he admits he's defeated by God!
Trv.1:	Yes! He will never accept that, so he's trapped!
All:	Hooray!!
Red:	Thank you all!
Trv.1:	Thank the Lord! *(They hear a muffled noise)*
Trv.3:	What's that?
Red:	It's coming from the cupboard! Hold on! *(Red opens cupboard and out leaps Grandma)*
Gran:	Where is he? Let me at him!
Red:	Gran!!
Gran:	Red! I thought the wolf had got you!

Red: I thought he'd got you! *(They hug)*

Trv.1:   He's got nobody!

Trv.2:   This calls for a party!

All: Yes!!

(Music starts for finale. All cast files on stage to take part)

"FINALE!"

First, crowd sings from opening song,
> Red riding hood went in the wood,
> did what she could, Red riding hood,
> Red riding hood learnt to be good,
> Lives as she should, Red riding hood!

Red steps forward and sings from "Big, bad wolf,"
> The wolf just tried to take me on,
> He should know my faith is strong,
> My God was with me all along, Tra la la la la!

> Lord, I'll do just as you say,
> Please let your words light my way,
> I'll worship you both night and day, Tra la la la la!
> Who's afraid of the big, bad wolf,
> The big, bad wolf, the big, bad wolf,
> Who's afraid of the big, bad wolf, Tra la la Not Me!!

Mum steps forward and sings from "His word,"
> Your Words are bread from heaven,
> Clear cool water for the soul,
> Soft as a whisper yet clear as a beacon,
> Help this land to attain your goal.

Red steps forward and sings from "No Compromise,"
> When I feel the danger rising,
> I call your name and you're by my side,
> I'll step with You than step with another,
> For Your love and mercy cannot be denied,
> You're the one who secured my freedom,
> Jesus Christ, the Name above all names!
> For you're the one who secured my freedom,
> Jesus Christ, the Name above all names!

The whole cast then sings "I Will Praise You."
Thank you Lord for showing me that though life can be hard
Your love for me will always see me through,
You are the king of everything, whatever comes my way,
I promise this thing I will do.
I will praise you (x3)
I will praise you with all of my heart.
Thank you for your Spirit Lord, my comforter and friend.
May the people know who you are too.
The Alpha and Omega, the beginning and the end.
Our Saviour, we worship you.
We will praise you (x3)
We will praise you with all of our heart.

END OF SCENE, ACT AND PANTOMIME.

THE END.

MOORLEY'S

...... are growing Publishers, adding several new titles to our list each year. We also undertake private publications and commissioned works.

Our range of publications
Includes: **Books of Verse**
Devotional Poetry
Recitations
Drama
Bible Plays
Sketches
Nativity Plays
Passiontide Plays
Easter Plays
Demonstrations
Resource Books
Assembly Material
Songs & Musicals
Children's Addresses
Prayers & Graces
Daily Readings
Books for Speakers
Activity Books
Quizzes
Puzzles
Painting Books
Daily Readings
Church Stationery
Notice Books
Cradle Rolls
Hymn Board Numbers

Please send a S.A.E. (approx 9" x 6") for the current catalogue or consult your local Christian Bookshop who should stock or be able to order our titles.

Red Riding Hood

Words and Music by Jeff Grist.

"RED RIDING HOOD!"

Intro.
```
     G    Bm   C      D     G     Bm    C       D
```

```
      G    Bm   C        D    G      Bm        C      D
(1.) Red riding hood -        said where she stood,
      G    Bm       C      D    G      Bm       C      D
     You must be good, Red riding hood.
        G       Bm    C     D   G    Bm      C      D
     It must be under-stood -    even if you could,
      G    Bm       C      D    G      Bm       C      D
     You must be good, Red riding hood.
```

```
      C    D     G           C      D       G
(2.) Red is only young -     Full of joy and fun.
      C      D     Bm      Em     C       D     G
     Sweet and inno-cent is she - as the day begun.
      C      D      G          C      D        G
     She just couldn't know -    how the day would go,
        C       D       Bm     Em      C                D
     The sands of time are falling and the level's getting low!
```

```
      G          Bm     C     D    G      Bm      C     D
(3.) You wonder if you should -    keep out of the wood,
      G     Bm       C      D    G     Bm   C     D
     You'd better be good, Red riding hood.
        G        Bm     C     D             G          Bm
     'Cause waiting in the wood -     the wolf'll get you if
        C        D
     he could,
      G    Bm       C      D    G      Bm     C     D
     You'd better be good, Red riding hood.
```

```
      C   D       G            C     D    G
(4.) Very soon you'll see -    who has the vic-to-ry.
        C    D      Bm      Em       C        D      G
     The bene-fit of righteous-ness and truth will set you free.
        C    D     G         C     D    G
     The wolf howls and cries - with evil in his eyes,
      C     D     Bm     Em       C              D
     Take no heed unto his words, don't listen to his lies.
```

```
     G    Bm   C     D    G     Bm   C      D
```

```
        C    D     G          C     D     G
(5.) Our little girly Red -   unfortun-ately said
      C        D       Bm     Em     C      D      G
     she would trust the hairy one and soon she is misled.
        C       D     G          C       D      G
     But because the Bible say - the dark was held at bay
        C     D     Bm              Em
     and Red and all her friends would see-
      C             D           E
     good will win the day-       -ay
```

```
      A    E    D      E     A      E     D      E
(6.) Any-body could -      keep out of the wood,
      A     E     D       E      A      E    D      E
     learn to live good, Red riding hood.
      A     E      D       E    A     E     D      E
     Live as you would -    or live as you should,
      A     E      D     E      A        E          D    E
     Live and do good, Red riding hood.
      A     E      D     E      A        E          D    E
     Live and do good, Red riding hood.
      A     E      D     E      A
     Live and do good, Red riding hood.
```

END.

Who's Afraid of the Big bad Wolf?

Words by Jeff Grist
Music by Ann Ronell

Repeat 3 times + end.

```
          F(G)                    G(D)
Chorus: Who's afraid of the big, bad wolf?
          G7(D7)                  F(G)
        The big, bad wolf? The big, bad wolf?
                                  G(D)
        Who's afraid of the big, bad wolf?
          G7(D7)        F(G)
        Tra la la la la!
```

(THIRD CHORUS: CHANGE KEY TO G.)

```
            F                  G
(1.)Red: Once the wolf came after me,
             G7                   F
         he thought he'd eat me for his tea,
                          G
         What a fearful sight to see.
         G7            F
  Crowd: Tra la la la la.
           F                  G
    Red: I asked him if he had a thirst,
             G7                   F
         suggest he drink some water first.
                              G
         Filled him up. Thought he would burst.
         G7            F
  Crowd: Tra la la la la.
```

(AFTER SECOND CHORUS, CHANGE KEY TO G.)

```
            G                  D
(2.)Red: What the wolf just didn't see,
             D7                G
         he thought he took water from me.
                          D
         I really gave him T.C.P.
         D7          G
  Crowd: Tra la la la la.
           G                      D
    Red: He walks the woods from length to breadth,
         D7                G
         can find no one to scare to death,
                              D
         'cause everyone can smell his breath.
         D7          G
  Crowd: Tra la la la la.
```

END.

His Word.

Words and Music by Jeff Grist.

```
                                    "HIS WORD."

        Bm                          Em                      Bm
(1.) The Bible's a book about prophets. -  There's bravery and
                    Em
     battles ga-lore.
            Bm                       Em              C
     But read it with more under-standing - to find out what it's
            D
     all for.

         G       D                   Em         C               G
(2.) His - word  -  is the book  -  of ages.
                        D            Em               C
     Inspired by God    -     and food - for the soul.
         G       D                   Em         C
     A light in darkness  - and sav- ing power.
     G       D           C       D
     Hope for men  - to a-chi-  eve
             G         D          Em        C         D
     their goal.

             Bm                      Em             Bm
(3.) It's about the works of the Father -  and of all the good
                        Em
     things He's done.
     Bm                       Em             C            D
     How he secured our sal-vation -   by sacrificing His Son.

     G       D           Em          C
(4.) His - word  - is a crush-ing hammer,
     G       D               Em          C
     life-giving force -  and  de-vour-ing flame.
     G       D               Em          C
     Loved by the saints,  - blessed seed for the sower.
     G       D       C   D   G       D       Em      C       D
     Trust-wor-thy and sur-e the same.

     Bm                          Em             Bm
(5.) It's full of Gods' great wonders. -  Incredible - miraculous
     Em
     tales.
             Bm              Em              C
     It holds promises never broken  - and a love that never
     D
     fails.

     G       D       Em          C
(6.) His - word - is full - of knowledge.
     G       D       Em              C
     Wisdom for aged  - wis-dom for  youth.
     G       D       Em          C
     Sword and pro-tector, - life pur-ifier,
     G       D       Em          C   D   G
     word of God,  -    hol-der of tru--u--th

     G       D           Em          C
     His - word  -  is the book  - of ages.
     G       D       Em                  C
     Inspired by God - and food - for - the soul.
         G       D               Em      C
     A light in darkness      and a sav-ing power.
     G       D       C   D           Em      A       C
     Hope for men - to a-chi-eve - their goal,
             D                   Em          A       C
     to a-chi-eve  - their goal,
             D           G
     to a-chi-eve  - their goal.

                            END.
```

Mum and Grandma's Song

Words and Music by Jeff Grist.

MUM AND GRANDMA'S SONG.

```
                D
(1.)Mum. You're my little girl, my life and my world,
                                      A7
         you fill my heart with joy.
         A7
Grandma. You made me a wreck, were a pain in the neck,
                                      D
         and besides, I wanted a boy!
         D
    Mum. You put a smile on my lips.
         D
Grandma. You put a mile on my hips.
         D7                                  G
    Mum. You make me complete through and through.
              G                        D
   Both. But there's no denying, and I wouldn't be lying,
                  A         D
         when I say that I love you.


                  D
(2.)Mum. I was once all forlorn, but then you were born,
                                      A
         and filled my world with light.
              A7
Grandma. I was reasonably happy 'till you filled your nappy,
                                      D
         and left me an 'orrible sight.
         D
    Mum. I watched you grow up.
         D
Grandma. I watched you throw up.
         D7                                  G
    Mum. There's nothing that I wouldn't do.
              G                        D
   Both. But there's no denying, and I wouldn't be lying,
                  A         G    G7
         when I say that I love you.


         G         Em    A         D    F#m    Bm
(3.)Mum. Ah -          the way that you look   -
                           Em              A
         the way that you speak,
                           D    D7
         you are just good as gold!
         G         Em    A         D    F#m    Bm
Grandma. Urgh -        you're a terrible cook   -
                                   E
         and the way that you shriek,
                           A    A7
         makes my blood turn cold.


                D
(4.)Mum. You gave me such pride when you sat at my side,
                                      A7
         and I sang as you slept in my lap.
         A7
Grandma. You gave me labour pains, and varicose veins,
                                      D
         and a belly that looks like a map.
         D
    Mum. Not to mention the smiles.
         D
Grandma. Not to mention the piles.
         D7                              G
    Mum. And the hugs and kisses too.
              G                        D
   Both. But there's no denying, and I wouldn't be lying,
                  A         D    D7
         when I say that I love you.
```

```
            G         Em    A                 D    F#m   Bm
(5.)Mum. Ah -          the things that you do  -
                             Em        A
         your sweet little ways,
                        D         D7
         you're a wonder to see.
            G         Em        A             D    F#m   Bm
Grandma. Urgh -       you're a silly young moo -
                             E
         but then one of these days,
                            A        A7
         you'll get old just like me, he! he!


            D
(6.)Mum. You're a gift from above, a showering of love,
                                        A
         we're a song and you are the verse.
                   A7
Grandma. With your shrieks and your yells, and your strange funny
                                        D
         smells, I wondered if life could get worse!
         D
    Mum. Sometimes life has been flat.
         D
Grandma. But despite all of that,
         D7                                  G
   Both. The one thing that always rings true.
               G                      D
   Both. Is that there's no denying, and I wouldn't be lying,
               A          D
         when I say that I love you.
```

END.

Don't Go Down To The Cakeshop Mum

Words and Music by Jeff Grist

"DON'T GO DOWN TO THE CAKE SHOP, MUM!!"
(TO BE SUNG "BARBERSHOP" STYLE!)

```
         D                                   G            D
(1.) When I was a little boy, my mother said to me,
         D                               E              A
     if you eat your greens and meat, there's ice cream after tea
       D                             G              D
     a sticky bun is lots of fun. We'll wash it down with pop,
       G            D  B7      E              A
     and follow it with biscuit and the odd chocolate drop.

         D                                   G          D
(2.) Don't go down to the cake shop mum, I've had enough to eat.
         D                          E            A
     I've had my fill of fairy cakes and other things so sweet.
              D                           G              G7
     There's flab and fat where muscle sat, my belly's on the floor,
       D                     F#   B7     E        A   D   A
     don't go down to the cake shop mum, I can't take any more!

         D                                   G             D
(3.) The breakfast treat was shredded wheat with strawberries and cream,
         D                          E              A
     buttered toast, ham honey roast and pancakes by the ream,
       D                       G            D
     chicken legs, chips and eggs would quickly follow brunch,
       G           D      B7      E          A
     a four course meal of lamb and veal would satisfy for lunch.

         D                                   G          D
(4.) Don't go down to the cake shop mum, I'm feeling rather sick,
         D                     E        A
     if I eat another cake, I'll look like Moby Dick!
         D                      G             G7
     Captain Ahab will try to stab the mountain that is me.
       D                     F#   B7       E   A       D  A
     Don't go down to the cake shop mum, I've had enough for tea.

         D                                   G          D
(5.) Next at three, afternoon tea of bread and bramble jam,
         D                          E              A
     a little snack, and then a rack of ribs from roasted lamb,
           D                        G            D
     we're in the mood for Chinese food with chicken chop suey.
         G            D        B7       E              A
     What would be nice is special fried rice, in fact a meal for three!

         D                                   G          D
(6.) Don't go down to the cake shop mum, I've no hunger or thirst
       D                         E             A
     if anything should pass my lips, I think that I would burst!
       D                           G            G7
     Believe or not, my teeth have rot, my heart is asking "Why?"
       D                     F#   B7     E        A   D
     Don't go down to the cake shop mum, I think I'd rather die!!
       D                     F#   B7     E        A   D
     Don't go down to the cake shop mum, I think I'd rather die!!
```

END.

Stay on the Path of Truth

Words and Music by Jeff Grist

"STAY ON THE PATH OF TRUTH."

Mum sings,

```
         D         G       C    G                     C        D       G  G7
(1.)     Now you're going on a journey and you'll be all on your own,
         C                G            A              D
         travelling past deception woods, miles from any phone.
           G    C      D               C     D   G    G7
         Be courteous to who you meet but never ever stop.
         C                G                   C         D         G
         Go straight through until the end. Don't let your standards drop.
```

```
                C                               G                 E
Chorus:  Wherever life will take you, let this be your journeys' guide,
         C         D            C       D      G
         stay on the path of truth and don't go off the side.
```

```
         D    G      C    G                 C        D       G  G7
(2.)     Though lying's very tempting, let me tell you 'bout our Jim.
           C              G           A              D
         On a job application found it asked if he could swim.
           G    C      G               C     D      G  G7
         Well he really wanted work. He nearly said that this was so,
                  C              G           C    D     G
         but found out it was "Deep sea diving" and decided to say "No!"
```

```
         D  G      C          G             C    D    G    G7
(3.)     Now Pat had lunch down his local when he had his little scare,
                 C            G         A           D
         'cause his wife phoned up the barmaid to see if he was there.
           G    C    G             C     D    G    G7
         Said Pat, "You haven't seen me!" and he tucked into his grub.
              C             G                 C
         You can imagine his face when he found out that his wife phoned
         D      G
         from the pub!
```

```
         D    G    C     G                 C         D       G   G7
(4.)     Drunken Horace stumbled home one night. He'd slipped and cut his back.
         C                G        A             D
         Looked in the bathroom mirror to plaster up the crack.
           G    C    G           C    D     G    G7
         He hadn't woken Nelly. Crept to bed and thought he'd pass,
                C             G            C    D    G
         but the silly fool had missed and put the plaster on the glass.
```

Red sings,

```
           D  G     C     D              C      D     G  G7
(5.)     I've listened to your teaching and I'll do just as you say,
             C            G        A       D
         and I'll return as quickly by the end of the day.
           G    C       G         C    D     G     G7
         I really don't want to get lost where I can't be traced,
               C                   G           C  D      G
         Rest assured, I'll do my best not to be caught red-faced.
```

```
                         END.
```

Wolf's Song

Words and Music by Jeff Grist.

"THE WOLF'S SONG!"

Intro.

```
            Am    Em    Am    Em    Am    Em    Am    Em
```

```
              Am              Em              Am              Em
(1.)
Speak         Hi!                     It's me!
              Am              Em              Am              Em
Sing          Welcome to my world of obs-    cu-    ri-    ty.
                Am            Em       Am              Em
Speak         Oh hi!                   Again!
              Am              Em              Am       Em
Sing          Stop and have a chat. You can be my     friend.
              Dm                              E
              Everyone is equal here 'cause nobody's of worth.
                  Dm                                        E
              And by the time I'm finished here, you'll be damned upon
                            Am          Repeat intro.
              the earth, so Hi!
```

```
                Am                      Em              Am              Em
(2.)
Speak         Hello!                              Good day!
                Am                      Em              Am              Em
Sing          But that won't last too long if I-      have my      way
                Am                      Em              Am              Em
Speak         Bonjour!                                 Hola!
              Am                      Em              Am              Em
Sing          Chow,              Buenos dias, even       Bore       da.
              Dm                      E
              I know all the languages beneath this cursed sun.
                  Dm                                    E
              You can't say that I'm prejudiced 'cause I hate everyone,
                  Am                    Em              Am       Em
              so Ha!!                      (I mean Hi!)
                  Am                    Em              Am              Em
              My my!
```

```
              Gm                    E              Gm                      E
(3.)          People don't understand me. They think that killing's my goal,
                  Gm                  E              Dm                    E
              but that depends on my hunger! What I'm really after's your soul!
```

```
                Am                      Em              Am              Em
(4.)          So hi!                              Come in!
              Am                      Em              Am              Em
              Let me        -      introduce you to a   world of   sin.
                  Am                  Em              Am              Em
              This way!                          Follow me!
                    Am              Em              Am              Em
              There's wonders in the   wood. Just   -   come and - see.

              Dm                      E
              Step into the thicket and have a little nap.
              Dm                          E
              Then when you awaken, you'll find you're in my trap!
                  Am                    Em              Am              Em
              So hi!                              Oh hi!
                  Am                  Em              Am              Em
              My my!!
                  Am                  Em              Am              Em
              So hi!                              Oh hi!
                  Am                  Em              Am
              My my!
```

END.

No Compromise

Words and Music by Jeff Grist.

"NO COMPROMISE!"

```
Intro.
     C      F     G     F     C     F     G     F

     C                        F
(1.) Sitting alone in the dark of the woods,
     G                        F
     sift my way through the events of today,
     C                        F
     thinking of how I'd have handled things better,
       G                          F
     how differently things would have turned out that way.
       G                      F
     I've gone the road that I said I wouldn't,
       G              F        C     F     G     F
     your path for me lies up another way!

     C                        F
(2.) All of my trials are inconsequential
     G                        F
     when they're compared on the grand scale of things.
       C                        F
     To strengthen my guard would be preferential.
       G                      F
     To remain in your will. Temptation stings.
     G            F
     All I want is to be in your favour,
     G            F              C     F     G     F
     All I want is to be with the King of Kings.

     Am                            D
(3.) Lord, sometimes your path can be a lonely road,
               C        F           C        Em
     'specially when friends go a different way,
       Am                    D
     but who was with you when they hit the nails,
         C       F                   G        G7
     As you bore the price that was ours to pay!

     C                        F
(4.) In this place, wisdom spirals to madness
       G                    F
     and all your standards crumble to dust.
       G                    F
     Forgive me Lord and guide my steps,
       G                    F
     for by your Word, in you I can trust.
     G                        F
     You're the one who'll secure my freedom,
     G              F          C     F     G     F
     Jesus Christ, the Name above all Names!

     Am                            D
(5.) Lord, sometimes your path can be a lonely road,
               C        F           C        Em
     'specially when friends go a different way,
       Am                    D
     but who was with you when they hit the nails,
         C       F                   G        G7
     as you bore the price that was ours to pay!
```

```
            C                       F
(6.) Now as I feel that all seems against me,
         G                  F
     I feel your touch as you're by my side.
            C                   F
     Your Word is a lamp, a light that guides me.
            G                  F
     Your love and mercy cannot be denied.
            G                     F
     With all my strength I'll stand by your values,
     G                       F          C        F      G       F
     from now on, there'll be no compromise!
            G                     F
     With all my strength I'll stand by your values,
     G                    F             C
     from now on there'll be - no - compromise!

     F          G        F          C
```

                                        END.

Your Words Are Written On MY Heart.

Words and Music by Jeff Grist.

*After 2nd repeat of chorus, go to finale.

"YOUR WORDS ARE WRITTEN ON MY HEART!"

```
Intro.
      Em    C   Em    C   Em    C   Em    C   Em

      Em                          D
(1.) Caught out in the dark. I've never felt so scared.
          G        D          C
      I can feel the evil closing in.
  B7 Em                          D
      Walking round me now, I can see his sharp teeth bared,
      G        D          C
      hot breath   beating on my skin,
                B7     Em    Repeat intro sequence.
      beating on my skin.

      Em                                    D
(2.) I've lost your written word. It lies torn upon the ground,
            G        D          C
      and this creature has me in its' snare.
   B7       Em                                           D
      But as I think that there's no hope, and there's no help to

      be found,
          G        D          C
      I remem-ber    re-ading some-where,
      D                    Am       C  D
      words that really gave me hope in my sorrow,
      D                    Am       C  D
      lines that burst upon my soul, today, tomorrow,

              G        D          C
CHORUS. Your words are written on my heart.
        D    G       D       C
        There is nothing to keep us apart.
        D    G       D
        They are a guide to lead me,
          Em                C
        a lamp that lights my way,
              Em      D          C
        Living words that turn the night to day,
                D     Em    Repeat intro sequence.
        turn the night to day.

          Em                            D
(3.) You see the light shines brightly. You're dazzled by its' glare.
        G        D          C
     Now look at what you have be-come!
  B7       Em                          D
     You've grown used to the darkness. You've made your home in there.
        G        D          C
     Every-thing but hatred leaves you numb.

      D                              Am         C  D
      Don't be scared. Please come near. It won't hurt you.
      D                    Am            C  D
      Let the darkness    disappear. I won't desert you.
```

```
        G              D               C
CHORUS. His words can be written on your heart.
     D      G         D          C
     There is nothing to keep you apart.
     D       G       D
     They are a guide to lead you.
        Em                 C
     A lamp that lights your way
           Em        D              C
     Living words that turn the night to day.
              D     Em    C    Em      C
     Turn the night to day.


     C                  D              Bm
(4.) You can't run or fight, can't escape the light.
                     Em          D     C
     It's time to face the demons eating you inside.
                  D               Bm
     Time to turn away, hold the dark at bay,
                  B7                       Em
     Time to start to day, let Him light your way.

     Quietly repeat intro sequence.

     (BREAK FOR SCRIPT.)

     C                 D              Bm
(5.) A new day's begun, started by the one
                      Em      D    C
     Who's love        endures for evermore.
                  D                        Bm
     Time to leave this place, cleansed without a trace,
                  B7
     by our loving King.


        B7             G       D       C
CHORUS. Whose words are written on our heart,
     D      G         D          C
     there is nothing to keep us apart.
     D      G        D
     They are a guide to lead us,
       Em                 C
     a lamp that lights our way,
          Em        D               C
     living words that turn the night to day,
              D     Em
     turn the night to day.
                        Fade to end.
```

I Will Praise You

Words and Music by Jeff Grist

"FINALE SONGS!"

First, crowd sings (from opening song)
```
G   Bm    C     D    G    Bm     C     D
Red riding hood-      went in the wood,
G   Bm    C         D    G    Bm    C       D
did what she could, Red riding hood.
G   Bm    C    D    G     Bm     C     D
Red riding hood-       learnt to be good.
G    Bm     C         D              G
Lives as she should, Red riding hood!
```

Red steps forward and sings (from "Big, bad wolf")
```
G                      D
The wolf just tried to take me on,
D7                     G
He should know my faith is strong,
G              D         D7          G
My God was with me all along, Tra la la la la!
G                     D
Lord, I'll do just as you say,
     D7              G
Please let your Words light my way,
     G              D        D7          G
I'll worship you both night and day, Tra la la la la!
G                    D              D7
Who's afraid of the big, bad wolf, the big, bad wolf,
     G
the big, bad wolf.
G                    D         D7          G
Who's afraid of the big, bad wolf, tra la la not me!!
```

Mum steps forward and sings (from "His Word!")
```
G       D           Em          C
Your - words -   are bread -  from Heaven,
G       D           Em          C
Clear cool water   -   for  - the soul,
G       D           Em          C
Soft as a whisper - yet clear - as a beacon,
G       D           C   D        G
Help this land       to atta-in    your goal!
```

Red steps forward again and sings (from "No compromise!")
```
C             F
When I feel the danger rising,
G             F
I call your name and you're by my side,
C             F
I'll step with you than step with another,
   G              F
For your love and mercy cannot be denied,
G             F
You're the one who secured my freedom,
G             F           G
Jesus Christ, the Name above all names!
```

The whole cast step forward and sing "I will praise you!"

```
G                      C              D                G
Thank you Lord for showing me that though life can be hard,
   G                C            D
Your love for me will always see me through,
   G                C              D                G
You are the King of ev'rything, whatever comes my way,
   C          D            G           C   D
I promise this thing I will do.
        G        C        D
I will pra-  ai- aise you,
        G        C        D
I will pra-  ai- aise you,
        G        C        D
I will pra-  ai- aise you,
        C              D          G           C   D
I will praise you with all of my heart.

G                   C              D              G
Thank you for your Spirit, Lord, my comforter and friend,
G              C              D
May the people know who you are too,
   G          C            D              G
The alpha and omega, the beginning and the end,
   C          D        G           C   D
Our saviour, we wor-ship you.
         G        C        D
We will pra-  ai-  aise you,
                  C          D
We will pra-  ai-  aise you,
         G        C          D
We will pra-  ai-  aise you,
         C              D          G
We will praise you with all of our heart.
```

END.